Independently published

ISBN: 9783911386111

© Gianfranco Conti & Dylan Viñales 2024

A New GCSE Spanish Workbook

Part One

Gianfranco Conti, Dylan Viñales & Ana del Casar

Edited by Inés Głowacka

A New GCSE Spanish Workbook

This workbook is for students and teachers preparing for the GCSE Spanish exams beginning in 2026 (first teaching September 2024). It is the first of two books covering a total of 10 thematic areas.

Each one of the five units in this book consists of the following:

1. Foundation Tier vocabulary building exercises.
2. Foundation Tier exam-style reading tasks.
3. Higher Tier vocabulary building exercises.
4. Higher Tier exam-style reading tasks.
5. A Grammar Focus section with explanations and practice exercises.
6. Pre-speaking and writing exercises.
7. An exam-style photo task for both tiers.
8. An exam-style role-play task for both tiers.
9. Exam-style writing tasks for both tiers.
10. Two banks of model sentences, one for each tier.

At the end of the workbook, there is a set of answers to the exercises from parts 1-6 above.

We know how important frequent repetition is for students of all levels of proficiency. Therefore, each unit has been carefully planned to recycle the same words, chunks and sentences many times over to help students remember as much as possible when they do the exam. In addition, many high-frequency vocabulary items and grammatical structures are encountered across all the units.

The content has been written to take account of the DfE's requirement that GCSE students become familiar with aspects of the contexts and cultures in which Spanish is spoken. The comprehension texts were written by the authors, often drawing on authentic sources.

Thematic, vocabulary and grammar content has been matched against the new specifications and should be suitable for any of the three awarding bodies: AQA, Eduqas and Pearson-Edexcel. We have stuck closely to the word lists provided by the awarding bodies, but allowed ourselves some leeway, for instance where we felt more vocabulary is needed to let students express themselves more completely. For example, in the Healthy Lifestyle unit we added words such as *alimentación, proteínas* and *vapear*, which are absent from defined word lists. In the Environment unit we included words such as *renovable, energía eólica* and *sufrimiento*. In the Media and Technology Unit we included *disponible, herramienta* and *pinchar*. Some words outside the defined lists are glossed.

How to use the book

Students may work through the whole book, or teachers may like to photocopy individual pages, sections or whole units. Teachers or students can use the answers provided for checking or marking.

Acknowledgement

We are grateful to our editor Inés Głowacka for her work proof-reading and editing this document, as well as her input into the content of the comprehension texts.

Thank you to Steve Smith for his work on the original volume **A New GCSE French Workbook - Part One** and for his support in the creation of this Spanish edition.

Additionally, our gratitude to our team of incredible educators who helped in checking all the units of this volume: Ana Amores Márquez, Anneliese Yafai, Aurélie Lethuilier, Christian Moretti, Jérôme Nogues, Laura García Gracia, María Valverde & Simona Gravina. It is thanks to your time, patience, professionalism and detailed feedback that we have been able to produce such a refined and highly accurate product.

Gianfranco, Dylan & Ana

Contents

UNIT 1

Healthy living

Contents

- Foundation vocab building.
- Foundation reading.
- Higher vocab building.
- Higher reading.
- Grammar focus – the Perfect Tense.
- Preparing for speaking and writing.
- Writing and speaking from a photo card.
- Speaking in a role play.
- Writing.
- Sentence bank.

Foundation vocab building

Vocabulary

el agua (f)	water
la alimentación	food
a menudo	often
beber	to drink
bueno/a	good
cada	every, each
comer	to eat
cuello	neck
la comida	meal
el corazón	heart
el cuerpo	body
deber	to have to
el dolor	pain, ache
en forma	fit
equilibrado/a	balanced
la forma física	fitness
fumar	to smoke
intentar	to try
la leche	milk
malo/mala	bad
mejorar	to get better
el pan	bread
el pescado	fish
las verduras	vegetables
pienso que	I think that
saludable	healthy
vapear	to vape
vivir	to live
zumo	juice

1. Match up.

El corazón	Fish
El cuerpo	Diet
Malo	Good
El pescado	Heart
Bueno	To get better
El dolor	Fit
Dieta	To vape
Mejorar	Bad
Deber	To live
Vapear	To have to
En forma	Body
Vivir	Pain

2. Broken words.

a. Fu _ _ _   To smoke
b. E_ f _ _ma   Fit
c. B _ _ n_   Good (m)
d. Beb _ _   To drink
e. La l _ _ _e   Milk
f. Ca _ _   Every / each
g. In_ _ _ _ar   To try
h. Co_ _ _a   Meal
i. Va_ _ _r   To vape
j. Ma _ _   Bad

3. Gapped translation.

a. Estoy en forma.   I am _ _ _.
b. Fumo mucho.   I _ _ _ _ _ a lot.
c. Pienso que…   I _ _ _ _ _ that.
d. Como demasiado.   I _ _ _ too much.
e. Tengo una dieta equilibrada.   I have a _ _ _ _ _ _ _ _ diet.
f. Como mucho pan.   I eat a lot of _ _ _ _ _.
g. No me gusta el pescado. I don't like _ _ _ _.

4. Faulty translation – spot and correct the wrong translations.

a. Como demasiado pan.   *I eat too much pasta.*
b. El azúcar es bueno para los dientes.   *Sugar is bad for your teeth.*
c. Normalmente como pescado.   *I rarely eat fish.*
d. Me encanta la carne.   *I hate meat.*
e. Mi cuello está regular.   *My neck is fine.*
f. Sigo una dieta equilibrada.   *I follow an unhealthy diet.*
g. Estoy en forma.   *I am unfit.*

5. Anagrams

a. etdia (diet)   _____
b. mciado (meal)   _____
c. riviv (to live)   _____
d. rfoam (fitness)   _____
e. raúczra (sugar)   _____
f. alom (bad)   _____
g. nap (bread)   _____
h. elche (milk)   _____

6. Complete the categories below with 3 words that belong to them.

a. Alimentación (food):

b. Adjetivos (adjectives):

c. Verbos (verbs):

d. Bebidas (drinks):

7. Translate into English.

a. Azúcar: s_____
b. Malo: b_____
c. Verduras: v_____

d. En forma: f_____
e. Bueno: g_____
f. Dieta: d_____

g. Intentar: t_____
h. Pan: b_____
i. Dolor: p_____

8. Complete the translation.

a. Tengo una _____ salud (I am in good health)

b. A menudo _____ verduras (I often eat vegetables)

c. Evito _____ (I avoid sugar)

d. Hago deporte _____ ____ _____ (I do sport every day)

e. No bebo _____ (I don't drink alcohol)

f. Debes proteger el _____ (You must protect the heart)

g. La comida rápida es _____ para la salud. (Fast food is bad for health)

h. Mi madre es muy _____ (My mother is very active)

9. Add in the missing letters.

a. _uerpo (body)

b. _gua (water)

c. _vitar (to avoid)

d. _alo (bad)

e. _ueno (good)

f. _quilibrado (balanced)

g._escado (fish)

h. _eche (milk)

10. Multiple choice – circle the right option.

a. To smoke	beber	fumar	comer
b. Body	forma	cuerpo	corazón
c. To avoid	dejar	salir	evitar
d. Meal	comer	comida	malo
e. Bad (f)	mala	buena	beber
f. Alcohol	alcol	alcool	alcohol
g. Good (m)	bueno	buen	bien
h. To try	beber	deber	intentar
i. To vape	fumar	vapear	comer
j. Health	sano	enfermedad	salud
k. Every/each	menudo	cada	nunca

11. Definitions

a. A food beginning with C: _____

b. A drink beginning with L: _____

c. A verb beginning with E: _____

d. An organ beginning with C: _____

e. A verb beginning with M: _____

f. The opposite of "bueno": _____

g. A verb beginning with B: _____

h. A food beginning with V: _____

i. A verb beginning with V: _____

j. A food beginning with P: _____

12. Break the flow and translate – mark the gaps and translate.

a. Sigo/una/dieta/equilibrada = I follow a healthy diet.

b. Comomuchaverdura = _____

c. Hagodeporteamenudo = _____

d. Normalmentesoyactiva = _____

e. Intentonofumarmucho = _____

f. Nuncabeboalcohol = _____

g. Estoyenforma = _____

h. Megustamucholacarne = _____

i. Amenudocomocomidarápida = _____

13. Spot and correct the spelling mistakes.

a. Vapar (to vape) _____

b. Intentatar (to try) _____

c. Alcol (alcohol) _____

d. Deta (diet) _____

e. Melo (bad) _____

f. Peskado (fish) _____

g. Ejercicyo (exercise) _____

h. Salut (health) _____

i. Carme (meat) _____

14. Translate into English.

a. Creo que hay que tener una dieta saludable. _____

b. Como bastante mal porque tomo demasiado azúcar. _____

c. Necesito comer menos dulces. _____

d. Estoy en forma porque hago mucho ejercicio. _____

e. Mi abuela es muy activa, ella sale a menudo. _____

f. No bebo alcohol pero vapeo un poco. _____

Foundation reading

1. **Look at the following comments about fitness apps.**

> **Sandra**
> Con mi aplicación hago preguntas a expertos sobre cómo mantenerme en forma. ¡Es genial!
>
> **Carlos**
> Con mi aplicación puedo comparar mi ejercicio con el de mis amigos. La competencia entre nosotros me motiva mucho.
>
> **Marta**
> Mi aplicación me ayuda mucho a organizar mis ejercicios cada semana. A menudo recibo alertas.
>
> **Mercedes**
> Mi aplicación mide la cantidad de kilómetros que corro cada día. Es fácil de usar y es muy útil para mí.
>
> **Andrés**
> Mi aplicación me anima a hacer ejercicio. Ofrece ideas diferentes y programas nuevos.

Who said...?

a. They can compare their exercise with others. _____
b. The app is easy to use. _____
c. The app lets you ask questions. _____
d. The app suggests new exercise programmes. _____
e. They get alerts from the app. _____

2. **People are giving advice on how to stay healthy. Complete the sentences.**

> **Amador**
> Evito la carne porque creo que la dieta vegetariana es mejor para mantenerse en forma. Por otro lado, los fines de semana paso tiempo con mis amigos. Es importante salir y divertirse para sentirse bien.
>
> **Luis**
> El deporte es muy importante. Si hacemos ejercicio regularmente en lugar de pasar horas frente a una pantalla, tenemos más posibilidades de mantenernos en forma.
>
> **Ana**
> Paso mucho tiempo descansando mientras escucho música y leo. También me gusta montar en bicicleta con mis amigas. Es bueno para mejorar la forma física.

a. Amador _____ meat because the vegetarian diet is better for _____ _____. He says it's important to _____ _____ and _____ _____ in order to feel well.

b. Luis thinks it's better to _____ _____ than spend hours in _____ of a _____.

c. Ana likes to relax while _____ to _____ and _____. She also likes _____ with her friends.

Foundation reading

3. **Read this article about a popular street sport. Then answer the questions in English.**

El baloncesto 3x3 es una versión simplificada del baloncesto. Se juega en media cancha con dos equipos de tres jugadores cada uno. El juego es rápido y cada partido o bien dura 10 minutos, o bien termina si un equipo alcanza los 21 puntos. Este deporte de calle fue incluido en los Juegos Olímpicos de 2020, lo que muestra que es cada vez más popular. Da igual si ya juegas al baloncesto o si es algo nuevo para ti, con el baloncesto 3x3 te diviertes y mejoras como jugador.
*cancha = pitch, court

a. What is said about the pitch the game is played on? _____

b. When does a match end? Mention two points. _____

c. What shows that the sport is getting more popular? _____

d. What kind of players is the sport for? Mention two points. _____

4. **Carmen writes about her diet. Tick off the sentences which are correct.**

Cada mañana, empiezo mi día con un desayuno equilibrado, rico en proteínas y frutas. Prefiero alimentos frescos y naturales. Hago ejercicio con mucha frecuencia, por ejemplo, corro, monto en bicicleta o juego al baloncesto con mis amigos. Bebo mucha agua a lo largo del día. También duermo ocho horas cada noche, porque dormir bien es esencial para la salud. Por último, paso tiempo haciendo actividades que me gustan, como leer o tocar la guitarra, para mantener una buena salud mental. Creo que vivir de forma saludable consiste en encontrar un equilibrio entre la alimentación y el ejercicio.

a. Her breakfast contains protein and fruit.

b. She prefers natural food.

c. She rarely does exercise.

d. She goes walking with her friends.

e. She drinks lots of water throughout the day.

f. She has difficulty sleeping.

g. She finds reading good for her mental health.

h. Living healthily is about getting the balance between diet and exercise right.

Foundation reading

5. A doctor gives advice about exercise. Answer the questions in English.

> Aquí tenéis las ideas para mantenerse en forma y tener una buena salud.
>
> - Hacer deporte tres veces por semana durante veinte minutos. Algunas actividades que se pueden hacer sono caminar, montar en bicicleta y correr.
>
> - Nadar es una excelente manera de mantener el corazón en buena salud.
>
> - No quedarse sentado durante mucho tiempo, por ejemplo no estar delante del ordenador más de una hora sin levantarse.

   a. How often should you exercise and how long for? (Mention two points).

   (i) _____   (ii) _____

   b. Which activity is said to be a great way to keep fit? _____

   c. What should you not do? _____

6. Miguel Ángel talks about exercise.

> Hago mucho deporte últimamente. El sábado pasado, di una vuelta en bicicleta con mis amigos en el campo cerca de mi casa.
>
> El domingo fui a nadar al polideportivo. Allí hay una cafetería, así que también tomé una comida saludable.
>
> El lunes después del instituto jugué al baloncesto. Fue divertido pero estaba cansado después.
>
> El próximo sábado voy a dar un largo paseo con mis padres. Vamos a caminar al menos 10 kilómetros.
>
> En mi opinión, es importante ser lo más activo posible.

Complete the gap in each sentence using a word from the box below. There are more words than gaps.

tired	cycling	jogging	walking
swimming	dance	happy	sailing

   a. On Saturday he went _____

   b. On Sunday at the sports centre, he did _____

   c. After basketball he was _____

   d. Next Saturday he will go _____

Higher vocab building

Vocabulary

la alimentación	*food*
almorzar	*to have lunch*
el azúcar	*sugar*
la bebida	*drink*
la carne	*meat*
casero/a	*home-made*
la comida	*food*
el consejo	*advice*
el consumo	*consumption*
convertirse en	*to become*
descansar	*to rest*
dormir	*to sleep*
dulce	*sweet*
enfermo	*ill, sick*
la enfermedad	*illness*
esperar	*to hope*
el éxito	*success*
la grasa	*fat*
mantenerse en forma	*to keep fit*
nadar	*to swim*
poco sano	*not healthy*
el paseo	*stroll/walk*
recientemente	*recently*
reducir	*to reduce*
la salud	*health*
saludable	*healthy*
sin	*without*
sentir(se)	*to feel*
el tiempo	*time*
vegano/a	*vegan*
vegetariano/a	*vegetarian*

1. Match up.

Dieta	Sweet
Poco sano	Meat
Hacerse	Diet
Azúcar	Time
Tiempo	Not healthy
Paseo	Illness
Carne	To become
Consejo	Drink
Enfermedad	Advice
Bebida	A walk
Dulce	Sugar

2. Broken words.

a. Ca_ _ _   (meet)
b. Es_ _ _ _ _   (to hope)
c. S_ _   (without)
d. Az_ _ _ _   (sugar)
e. Na_ _ _   (to swim)
f. Dor_ _ _   (to sleep)
g. Tiem_ _   (time)
h. Be_ _ _ _   (drink)
i. Se_ _ _ _se   (to feel)
j. Con_ _ _ _   (advice)

3. Gapped translation.

a. Pasearse: To go _____
b. Mantenerse en forma: To keep _____
c. Almorzar sano: Eat a _____ lunch
d. Evitar comida grasienta: To avoid _____
e. Una bebida dulce: A _____ drink
f. Ser vegano: To be _____
g. Un café sin azúcar: A coffee _____ sugar
h. Reducir el estrés: To _____ stress

4. Faulty translation – spot and correct the wrong translations.

a. Una dieta equilibrada es necesaria: A diet coke is necessary.
b. Bebí una bebida dulce: I drank a healthy drink.
c. Intento perder peso: I manage to gain weight.
d. Él está muy enfermo: He is very tired.
e. ¿Qué me recomiendas?:   What do you think about me?
f. Me hice vegetariano: I will become vegetarian.

5. Definitions.

a. Opuesto de "salado": d_____
b. Comida: a _____
c. No come carne: v_____
d. Relajarse: d_____
e. Para una buena salud: s_____
f. No despertarse: d_____
g. Hay que: s___ d_____
h. Comer o beber: t_____
i. Opuesto de "con": s_____

6. Complete the categories.

a. 4 verbs:

b. 3 adjectives:

c. 4 nouns:

d. 1 adverb:

7. Translate into English.

a. Consejo: _____
b. Pasear: _____
c. Tiempo: _____
d. Reducir: _____
e. Azúcar: _____
f. Hacerse: _____
g. Esperar: _____
h. Descansar: _____
i. Nadar: _____

8. Complete with the correct option.

a. Hay que seguir una _____ equilibrada.

b. _____ deporte tres veces por semana.

c. Me gusta _____ por el campo.

d. Soy _____.

e. Mi madre es muy _____.

f. _____ fumar y beber alcohol.

g. Cuando tengo _____ salgo a correr por el parque.

h. Me encanta _____ en la piscina.

i. Me _____ tomar un café con azúcar.

| pasear |
| evito |
| activa |
| gustaría |
| dieta |
| tiempo |
| nadar |
| vegetariano |
| hago |

9. Add in the missing letters.

a. Un pa_eo lar_o   (a long walk)

b. Po_o s_no   (unhealthy)

c. Be_ida   (drink)

d. T_empo   (time)

e. Conse_o   (advice)

f. _onvertirse   (to become)

g. V_gano   (vegan)

h. Dulc_   (sweet)

10. Multiple choice – circle the right option.

a. Consejo	worry	advice	diet
b. Dormir	to sleep	to swim	to advice
c. Comer	to sleep	to keep	to eat
d. Esperar	to worry	to cry	to hope
e. Enfermo	worried	ill	tired
f. Azúcar	hope	sugar	healthy
g. Carne	ill	sleep	meat
h. Tiempo	time	sugar	meat
i. Sentir	to feel	to swim	to hope
j. Nadar	to hope	to sleep	to swim

11. Find the word

a. A food beginning with A: _____

b. A noun beginning with C: _____

c. A verb beginning with D: _____

d. A sport beginning with N: _____

e. A verb beginning with E: _____

f. The opposite of "hace tiempo": _____

g. Another word for "comida": _____

h. The similar of "vegano": _____

i. The opposite of "sano": _____

12. Translate into English.

a. La semana pasada estaba enfermo. _____

b. He cambiado mi dieta. _____

c. Hay que consumir menos azúcar. _____

d. Intento evitar las bebidas dulces. _____

e. Empecé a nadar dos veces por semana. _____

f. A menudo hago largos paseos por el campo. _____

13. Transpuzzle - arrange the sentences in the correct word order and translate them into English.

a. El gente de obesa aumenta número: _____

b. cambiar Decidí dieta mi: _____

c. Hay alimentos que más comer sanos: _____

d. no ponerme Espero enfermo: _____

e. Empecé montaña a largas hacer caminatas en la: _____

f. pongo No en mi azúcar café: _____

g. Me hacer más gustaría ejercicio: _____

h. Una las previene alimentación enfermedades buena: _____

i. me médico Mi ha hacerme vegano aconsejado: _____

Higher reading

1. **Read these ten pieces of advice from a website about healthy living.**

1. *Dieta equilibrada:* Comer mucha fruta, verdura y comida rica en proteínas.
2. *Beber*: Beber mucha agua a lo largo del día.
3. *Hacer ejercicio*: Intentar hacer por lo menos 30 minutos de ejercicio físico cada día.
4. *Dormir lo suficiente*: Dormir entre 7 y 9 horas cada noche.
5. *Evitar azúcar*: No consumir grandes cantidades de azúcar o alimentos procesados*.
6. *No fumar*: Evitar fumar (y no beber alcohol).
7. *Gestionar** bien el estrés*: Practicar técnicas de relajación como meditación y yoga.
8. *Pasar tiempo al aire libre*: Tomar un poco de sol y aire fresco cuando sea posible.
9. *Hacerse chequeos regulares*: Visitar al médico con regularidad para realizar controles de salud.
10. *Ser positivo*: Mantener una actitud optimista ante la vida.

   * alimentos procesados = processed foods   ** gestionar = to handle, deal with

In your own words summarise the basic advice below in note form in English.

1.	6.
2.	7.
3.	8.
4.	9.
5.	10.

2. **Samuel, who lives in Bolivia, describes what he eats most days. Read, then complete the paragraph in English.**

Empiezo cada día con un desayuno saludable de pan casero y fruta. Me gusta jugar al fútbol con mis amigos después de la escuela, es lo que me mantiene activo. Bebo mucha agua, especialmente durante los meses calurosos. Para la cena, mi familia y yo solemos comer arroz con muchas verduras.

He begins _____ day with a _____ breakfast consisting of _____ bread and fruit.

He enjoys _____ with his friends _____, which allows him to _____

He drinks _____, especially during the _____. For dinner, he and his family often

eat _____ with _____

Higher reading

3. **Read this website article which offers fitness advice to wheelchair users. Then answer the questions in English.**

Si utilizas una silla de ruedas*, volverte más activo mejorará tu salud y también puede ayudarte en tu vida diaria. Trata de elegir actividades que mejoren la salud del corazón y la fuerza muscular.

Todos los adultos de 19 a 64 años, incluidos los usuarios de sillas de ruedas, deben realizar al menos 150 minutos por semana de actividad, con ejercicios de entrenamiento de pesas** dos o más días a la semana.

La actividad física regular es buena tanto para la salud física como la mental y puede ser una excelente manera de conocer gente nueva.

Sin embargo, presta atención porque el uso de una silla de ruedas puede dificultar la realización de actividad física. También puede causar ciertos problemas médicos.

Algunas ideas de actividades deportivas son:

- Natación.

- Ejercicios sentados en sillas de ruedas.

- Carreras en silla de ruedas en el estudio o en la pista.

- Deportes de equipo.

* silla de ruedas = wheelchair   ** pesas = weights

---

1. What two advantages of physical exercise are mentioned near the beginning of the article?

   a) _____   b) _____

2. How much exercise should be done? _____

3. What other advice is given to all 19 to 64 year-olds, including wheelchair users?

   _____

4. What other advantage is mentioned, apart from physical health? _____

5. What warning is given for wheelchair users specifically?

   _____

6. What type of sport is recommended? _____

Higher reading

4. Read this advice about reducing stress.

1. Haz regularmente pausas cortas para relajarte.

2. Respira profundamente. Practica la respiración profunda* para calmar tu mente** y tu cuerpo.

3. Haz ejercicio. La actividad física ayuda a reducir el estrés.

4. Escucha música tranquila. Las melodías suaves pueden relajarte.

5. Haz una lista de tus actividades y decide cuáles son las más importantes a completar.

6. Habla con alguien. Comparte tus problemas con un amigo o alguien de tu familia para calmarte.

*profundo/a = deep   **mente = mind

Summarise briefly in notes each of the six pieces of advice.

1. _____

2. _____

3. _____

4. _____

5. _____

6. _____

5. Read this message from Gerardo about changing habits. Complete the notes.

¡Hola! Soy Gerardo. Antes me encantaba la carne y la comía todos los días para cenar pero a menudo me dolía el estómago por la noche. Por eso, mi médico me recomendó cambiar la dieta. Ahora solo como verduras, frutas y arroz. Me siento mucho mejor, ¡siempre estoy con energía!

1. The effects of eating meat.   _____

2. His doctor's advice.   _____

3. What he eats now in the evening.   _____

4. How he feels now. Mention two points. _____

Grammar focus - Part 1 – The Preterite Tense

Talking or writing about past events – the Preterite Tense

When referring to things that **were completed in the past**, we usually use the **preterite tense** (called the *pretérito indefinido* in Spanish**)**. We often find the preterite tense used with time phrases like *ayer, el fin de semana pasado, el año pasado* or *hace dos semanas* (two weeks ago). In English think of: I play**ed**, I **ate**, I **went**.

Below are some examples of the preterite tense in use with translations on the right.

Ayer **hablé** con mis amigos.	Yesterday I **talked** to my friends.
Anoche **participé** en una competición de fútbol.	Last night I **participated** in a soccer competition.
Para la cena **preparé** una ensalada.	For dinner I **prepared** a salad.
Compré verduras en el supermercado.	I **bought** vegetables at the supermarket.
La semana pasada **escuché** un podcast sobre salud.	Last week I **listened** to a podcast about health.

To score high marks in the GCSE exam you need to be able to express yourself in the preterite tense.

Preterite tense of REGULAR AR verbs – most verbs in Spanish end in AR in the infinitive!		
HABLAR (to talk)	**BAILAR** (to dance)	**ESCUCHAR** (to listen)
Yo habl**é** (I spoke)	Bail**é**	Escuch**é**
Tú habl**aste** (you singular spoke)	Bail**aste**	Escuch**aste**
Él/ella/usted habl**ó** (he/she/you formal singular spoke)	Bail**ó**	Escuch**ó**
Nosotros/as habl**amos** (we spoke)	Bail**amos**	Escuch**amos**
Vosotros/as habl**asteis** (you plural spoke)	Bail**asteis**	Escuch**asteis**
Ellos/ustedes habl**aron** (they/you formal plural spoke)	Bail**aron**	Escuch**aron**

1. Match up.

Mejorar	To buy
Terminar	To train
Ganar	To improve
Necesitar	To help
Ayudar	To win
Apoyar	To need
Comprar	To smoke
Entrenar	To lose weight
Fumar	To rest
Engordar	To finish
Adelgazar	To put on weight
Descansar	To support

2. Complete with the correct preterite tense form.

a. Yo _____ verduras esta mañana (comprar).

b. La condición física de Juan no _____ (mejorar) porque no _____ (entrenar).

c. Ellos _____ mucho (fumar).

d. Nosotros _____ a Juan con la rutina de ejercicios (ayudar).

e. Yo _____ con mi padre (entrenar).

f. Vosotros _____ el torneo de fútbol (ganar).

3. Circle the correct preterite tense form.

a. Yo compr**é**/compr**aste**/compr**ó** carne.

b. Nosotros gan**amos**/gan**asteis**/gan**aron** peso.

c. Ustedes prepar**amos**/prepar**asteis**/prepar**aron** una tortilla.

d. ¡Tú descans**é**/descans**aste**/descans**ó** por diez horas!

e. Él no fum**é**/fum**aste**/fum**ó**.

f. Yo apoy**é**/apoy**aste**/apoy**ó** a mi equipo de fútbol favorito.

g. Ustedes termin**aron**/termin**ó**/termin**asteis** bien el entrenamiento.

Preterite tense of REGULAR ER/IR verbs

COMER (to eat)		BEBER (to drink)	ESCRIBIR (to write)	VIVIR (to live)
Yo comí (I ate)		bebí	escribí	viví
Tú comiste (you singular ate)		bebiste	escribiste	viviste
Él/ella/usted comió (he/she/you formal sing. ate)		bebió	escribió	vivió
Nosotros/as comimos (we ate)		bebimos	escribimos	vivimos
Vosotros/as comisteis (you plural ate)		bebisteis	escribisteis	vivisteis
Ellos/ustedes comieron (they/you formal plural ate)		bebieron	escribieron	vivieron

1. Circle the correct preterite tense form.

a. Yo comí/comiste/comío carne.

b. Nosotros perdimos/perdisteis/perdieron peso.

c. Ustedes comimos/comisteis/comieron pescado.

d. ¡Tú dormí/dormiste/durmió durante diez horas!

e. Él no bebí/bebieron/bebió alcohol ayer.

f. Yo aprendimos/aprendí/aprendió a hacer tortilla.

g. Ustedes decidimos/decidisteis/decidieron seguir un régimen muy estricto.

2. Complete with the correct preterite tense form.

a. Yo _____ verduras (comer).

b. Él no _____ en Madrid (vivir).

c. Ellos no _____ mucho (correr).

d. Nosotros _____ hacer el entrenamiento (decidir).

e. Yo _____ una carta a mi padre (escribir).

3. Complete the table.

Infinitive	Preterite Tense
Comprar	Yo compré
Entrenar	
	Yo engordé
	Yo comí
Beber	
Perder	
	Yo escribí
Vivir	
	Yo decidí

4. Add the missing letters to make the preterite.

a. Marcos compr_ muchas verduras la semana pasada.

b. Ella se levant_ tarde ayer.

c. Nosotros viv_ _ _ _ cerca del campo.

d. Mis primos no beb_ _ _ _ _ alcohol anoche.

e. Mi madre com_ _ carne anteayer.

f. La semana pasada yo escrib_ a mi entrenador personal.

g. Usted engord_ tres kilos el año pasado.

h. Yo perd_ cinco kilos.

5. Translate into English.

a. Yo perdí diez kilos. _____

b. Tú entrenaste en el gimnasio. _____

c. Usted comió muy sano. _____

d. Yo viví en el campo. _____

e. ¿Jugaste al fútbol ayer? _____

f. Vosotros engordasteis. _____

g. Ellos bebieron agua. _____

h. ¿Qué comieron ustedes? _____

i. Mi madre compró pescado _____

j. Yo no bebí café. _____

Preterite tense of KEY IRREGULAR verbs.

IR / SER (to go / to be)	HACER (to do)	TENER (to have)
Yo fu**i**	Yo hic**e**	Yo tuv**e**
Tú fu**iste**	Tú hic**iste**	Tú tuv**iste**
Él/ella/usted fu**e**	Él/ella/usted hi**zo**	Él/ella/usted tuv**o**
Nosotros fu**imos**	Nosotros hic**imos**	Nosotros tuv**imos**
Vosotros fu**isteis**	Vosotros hic**isteis**	Vosotros tuv**isteis**
Ellos/ustedes fu**eron**	Ellos/ustedes hic**ieron**	Ellos/ustedes tuv**ieron**

1. Circle the correct personal pronoun.

a. **Nosotros/Ellos/Yo** fueron al gimnasio.

b. **Tú/Yo/Usted** hice el ejercicio.

c. **Nosotros/Vosotros/Ellos** tuvimos que adelgazar.

d. ¿Fuiste **ella/tú/vosotros** al médico?

e. **Ustedes/Vosotros/Nosotros** fuimos a nadar.

f. ¿Qué hicisteis **tú/ustedes/vosotros** anteayer?

g. ¿Con quién fue **ella/tú/nosotros**?

h. **Ellas/Vosotros/Nosotros** no hicimos dieta.

2. Correct the mistakes in the words in bold.

a. Ella **hiciste** deporte todos los días.

b. Nosotros **fueron** al gimnasio a las cuatro.

c. Mi padre **tuve** un problema de corazón.

d. Mi hermana no **fueron** al hospital.

e. Mis padres **hicisteis** una receta muy sana.

f. ¿A qué hora **fuisteis** tú a la piscina?

g. ¿**Tuvo** los dos hermanos problemas de salud?

h. Yo no **tuvieron** entrenamiento ayer.

3. Insert the correct conjugated verb.

a. Yo _____ un curso de natación.

b. Tú _____ al gimnasio.

c. Usted _____ un café para su tío.

d. Nosostros nos _____ vegano.

e. Yo _____ tres horas de clase ayer.

f. Ella _____ a clase de boxeo.

hicimos	hice	fuiste
hizo	fue	tuve

4. Complete the sentences below.

a. Ayer yo _____ a un spa con mis amigos para relajarme.

b. Anteayer, vosotros _____ a una clase de yoga.

c. Recientemente, ella se _____ vegetariana.

d. El sábado pasado mis hermanos _____ al gimnasio.

e. La semana pasada, ellos _____ mucho ejercicio.

f. El mes pasado yo _____ una lesión en el brazo.

g. Recientemente usted _____ un problema de salud.

5. Complete with the missing letters.

a. Yo comp_ _ (I bought).

b. Nosotros fu_ _ _ _ (we went).

c. Ellos engord _ _ _ _ (they put on weight).

d. Ella hi _ _ (she did).

e. Vosotros fu _ _ _ _ _ _ (you went).

f. Ustedes beb _ _ _ _ _ (you drank).

6. Translate into Spanish.

a. You (S) lost weight - _____ _____

b. They (F) went to the gym - _____ _____ ___ _____

c. We ate pasta - _____ _____ _____

d. I went to yoga class - ____ _____ __ _____ ___ _____

e. They (M) worked out - _____ _____ _____

f. She did boxing - _____ _____ _____

Useful verbs with a FIRST PERSON spell change

Infinitive	English	1st Person	Example
Buscar	To look for	Bus**qué**	Ayer busqué una receta sana *(Yesterday I **looked for** a healthy recipe).*
Jugar	To play	Jug**ué**	Jugué al fútbol en el parque. *(I **played** football in the park).*
Pagar	To pay	Pag**ué**	Pagué 2 euros por el helado. *(I **paid** 2 euros for the ice cream).*
Practicar	To practise	Practi**qué**	Practiqué boxeo con mi amigo. *(I **practised** boxing with my friend).*

1. Match up.

Yo jugué	I looked for
Yo fui	I trained
Yo busqué	I put on weight
Yo hice	I lost weight
Yo entrené	I practised
Yo practiqué	I played
Yo engordé	I paid
Yo pagué	I had
Yo tuve	I went
Yo adelgacé	I did

2. Translate into English.

a. Yo hice.

b. Yo comí.

c. Yo busqué.

d. Yo practiqué.

e. Yo compré.

f. Yo bebí.

g. Yo nadé.

h. Yo tuve.

i. Yo adelgacé.

j. Yo jugué.

k. Yo fui.

l. Yo perdí.

m. Yo entrené.

n. Yo esquié.

Preterite tense of two key REFLEXIVE verbs

ACOSTARSE (to go to bed)	LEVANTARSE (to get up)
Yo **me** acost**é**	Yo **me** levant**é**
Tú **te** acost**aste**	Tú **te** levant**aste**
Él/ella/usted **se** acost**ó**	Él/ella/usted **se** levant**ó**
Nosotros **nos** acost**amos**	Nosotros **nos** levant**amos**
Vosotros **os** acost**asteis**	Vosotros **os** levant**asteis**
Ellos/ustedes **se** acost**aron**	Ellos/ustedes **se** levant**aron**

3. Complete the words.

a. Me aco _ _ _ a las nueve (acostarse).

b. Jade se lev _ _ _ _ temprano (levantarse).

c. ¿Te enco _ _ _ _ _ _ bien esta mañana? (encontrarse).

d. Ella se p _ _ _ en el salón (pesarse).

e. Nos lev _ _ _ _ _ _ _ tarde (levantarse).

f. Yo me la _ _ en el baño (lavarse).

g. ¿A qué hora te acost _ _ _ _? (acostarse)

4. Correct the translation errors.

a. Ellas se pesaron: We weighed themselves.

b. Ellos se fueron a la cama: We went to bed.

c. Ustedes se relajaron: She relaxed.

d. Nosotros nos relajamos: He relaxed.

e. Usted se fue a la cama: He went to bed.

f. Tú te pesaste: You (plural) weighed yourselves.

g. Vosotros os fuisteis a la cama: We went to bed.

Grammar focus – Part 2 – The Perfect Tense

Talking or writing about past events – the Perfect Tense

In Spanish, the **perfect tense** (pretérito perfecto) is typically used to express **actions or events that have occurred in the recent past** or **have relevance to the present moment**.

The preterite tense, that we saw in the last grammar section, is used to indicate **actions or events that took place at a specific point in the past and are considered completed**.

They can often be used interchangeably, and the usage is similar to English. Therefore, you can use the same tense as you would in English **"fui"** for *I went* and **"he ido"** for *I have gone.*

Here are some model sentences in the Perfect Tense:

Yo **he publicado** muchas fotos en mi perfil de Instagram esta semana.
*I **have posted** many photos on my Instagram profile this week.*

Los jugadores **han entrenado** juntos durante dos horas.
*The players **have trained** together for two hours.*

Ella **ha compartido** un vídeo de su último partido en Facebook.
*She **has shared** a video of her last match on Facebook.*

¿**Has visto** el gol que marcó Messi en el último partido?
Have you seen the goal Messi scored in the last match?

Perfect tense of REGULAR verbs – AR Verbs			
HABLAR (to talk)			**Other useful AR verbs**
(Yo)	He hablado	(I have talked)	Bailar – Bailado
(Tú)	Has hablado	(you have talked)	Cantar – Cantado
(Él/Ella)	Ha hablado	(he/she has talked)	Comprar – Comprado
(Usted)	Ha hablado	(you singular, formal, have talked)	Escuchar – Escuchado
(Nosotros)	Hemos hablado	(we have talked)	Estudiar – Estudiado
(Vosotros)	Habéis hablado	(you plural have talked)	Jugar – Jugado
(Ellos/Ellas)	Han hablado	(they have talked)	Nadar – Nadado
(Ustedes)	Han hablado	(you plural formal, have talked)	Tomar – Tomado

1. Circle the correct personal pronoun.

a. **Nosotros/Él/Yo** hemos nadado en la piscina.

b. **Tú/Yo/Ella** ha bailado con sus amigas.

c. **Nosotros/Vosotros/Ellos** han comprado agua.

d. ¿**Yo/Tú/Usted** ha tomado un café esta mañana?

e. **Ellos/Yo/Tú** he escuchado la radio hoy.

f. ¿**Tú/Ellos/Vosotros** habéis jugado antes?

g. ¿Con **ella/tú/nosotros** quién has salido anoche?

h. **Ellas/Ella/Yo** ha cantado muy bien esa canción.

i. **Ellos/Yo/Tú** han comprado un coche nuevo.

j. **Tú/Yo/Ella** he hablado por teléfono con mi amigo.

k. ¿**Yo/Tú/Usted** has estudiado para el examen?

2. Translate.

a. I have danced.

b. We have listened.

c. You *(tú)* have swum.

d. My mother has played tennis.

e. My parents have bought a car.

f. He has had a coffee.

g. We have bought water.

h. They have studied for *(durante)* two hours.

i. Have they played before?

j. I have studied for the exam.

k. She has danced with her friend.

Perfect tense of REGULAR verbs – ER/IR Verbs

Both **ER** and **IR** verbs share the same **IDO** ending.

E.g. COMER – he com**ido** *(I have eaten)* and VIVIR – he viv**ido** *(I have lived)*

COMER (to eat)			Other useful ER/IR verbs
(Yo)	He comido	(I have eaten)	Beber – Bebido
(Tú)	Has comido	(you have eaten)	Dormir – Dormido
(Él/Ella)	Ha comido	(he/she has eaten)	Ir – Ido
(Usted)	Ha comido	(you singular, formal, have eaten)	Poder – Podido
			Salir – Salido
(Nosotros)	Hemos comido	(we have eaten)	Seguir – Seguido
(Vosotros)	Habéis comido	(you plural have eaten)	Ser – Sido
(Ellos/Ellas)	Han comido	(they have eaten)	Subir – Subido
			Tener - Tenido
(Ustedes)	Han comido	(you plural formal, have eaten)	Vivir – Vivido

1. Match up.

He comido	I have gone
He bebido	I have uploaded
He salido	I have eaten
He subido	I have drunk
He dormido	I have followed
He vivido	I have gone out
He seguido	I have slept
He podido	I have had
He ido	I have been
He tenido	I have been able to
He sido	I have lived

2. Translate into English.

a. He salido.

b. Has ido.

c. Hemos vivido.

d. Habéis bebido.

e. He dormido.

f. Ella ha seguido.

g. Hemos podido.

h. He comido.

i. He sido.

j. Has podido.

k. Han salido.

l. He vivido.

m. Has dormido.

n. Han tenido.

3. Correct the mistakes in the words in bold.

a. Ella **has ido** al cine.

b. Nosotros **habéis ido** al gimnasio a las dos.

c. Yo **has tenido** un problema de salud.

d. Mi hermana no **he ido** al hospital.

e. Mis padres **hemos salido** esta noche.

f. ¿A qué hora **ha ido** tú a la playa?

g. ¿**Hemos tenido** los dos hermanos problemas de salud?

h. Tú **he dormido** toda la noche.

4. Correct the translation errors.

a. Ellas han comido: *We have eaten.*

b. Ellos no han podido ir: *They have been able to go.*

c. Usted ha salido: *You have gone out, mate.*

d. Nosotros hemos dormido: *They have slept.*

e. Él ha tenido un problema: *She has had a problem.*

f. Tú has seguido a un nuevo influencer de salud: *I have followed a new health influencer.*

g. Vosotros habéis ido al cine: *I have gone to the cinema.*

h. Hoy he comido bien: *Today you have eaten well*

5. Translate into Spanish.

a. I have listened.

b. We have gone out.

c. They have eaten.

d. You (singular) have gone to the beach.

e. You (plural) have drunk water.

f. I have followed a new influencer.

g. I have had a problem.

h. They have swum in the pool.

i. We have danced in the club *(discoteca)*.

j. I have slept all night.

Verbs with IRREGULAR past participles in the Perfect tense

Some common verbs are irregular in the Perfect Tense.

It is only the **participle (HABLADO/COMIDO)** that is affected.

KEY VERBS WITH IRREGULAR PAST PARTICIPLES

Abrir (to open)	**– abierto**	Morir (to die)	**– muerto**
Decir (to say/to tell)	**– dicho**	Poner (to put/to place)	**– puesto**
Descubrir (to discover)	**– descubierto**	Romper (to break)	**– roto**
Escribir (to write)	**– escrito**	Ver (to see)	**– visto**
Hacer (to do/to make)	**– hecho**	Volver (to return)	**– vuelto**

e.g. **He visto** esa película varias veces, ¡es muy buena!   *I **have seen** that film several times. It's very good!*
Mis amigos **han vuelto** de su viaje por Europa.   *My friends **have returned** from their trip in Europe*

---

1. Insert the correct conjugated verb.

a. Yo he _____ un curso de natación.

b. ¿Usted ha _____ la puerta?

c. Tú has _____ la película nueva de...

d. Nosostros hemos _____ una carta.

e. Yo he _____ a casa hace tres horas.

f. Ella ha _____ su móvil.

roto	visto	vuelto
escrito	hecho	abierto

2. Complete the sentences below with a logical verb.

a. Yo he _____ una carta a mi amigo en España.

b. Esta mañana, he _____ a mi amigo por la calle.

c. Recientemente, ella ha _____ muchas cosas.

d. He_____ a casa hace una hora.

e. La semana pasada, ellos han _____ mucho ejercicio.

f. El mes pasado los científicos han _____ una nueva especie de pingüino en la Antártida.

g. Mi amigo se ha _____ el brazo jugando al fútbol.

---

3. Complete with the missing letters.

a. Yo he _ _ _ _ mi móvil. (I have broken my phone)

b. Nosotros hemos _ _ _ _ _. (we have done)

c. Ellos han _ _ _ _ _ _. (they have returned)

d. Ella ha _ _ _ _ _ _ _. (she has written)

e. Vosotros habéis _ _ _ _ _. (you, plural, have seen)

f. Ustedes han _ _ _ _ _ _ _. (you have opened)

g. Mi hámster ha _ _ _ _ _ _ ☹ (my hamster has died)

h. ¿Tú has _ _ _ _ _ hola? (have you said hello?)

4. Translate into Spanish.

a. I have done a course - H____ h _____
u_____ c_____

b. You have returned from the gym - H_____
v_____ d____ g_____

c. We have done many things- H_____
h_____ m_____ c_____

d. Today I saw my friend- H____ h____
v_____ a m___ a_____

e. They have said hello- H____ d_____
h_____

---

5. Translate into Spanish.

a. I have broken my phone.

b. You have returned from school.

c. He has done many things today.

d. I have written a letter to my friend.

e. She has said hello.

f. My brother has discovered a new game.

g. They have opened the door.

h. This morning I have seen my friend.

Preparing for speaking and writing

1. Complete the table.

Español	Inglés
Vapear	
	Vegetables
No es saludable	
	Vegetarian
El senderismo	
	Good health
Mi plato favorito	
	A healthy diet
Una buena comida	
	Recently
Es malo	
	I sleep
Yo evito	

2. Gapped translation.

a. Yo _____ frutas y verduras.

b. Para mantenerme en forma hago mucho deporte al aire _____.

c. Yo _____ una dieta sana.

d. Mi plato favorito _____ el pollo asado.

e. No bebo café por la _____.

f. No fumo pero sí _____.

g. Últimamente _____ más ejercicio.

h. _____ el pescado a la carne.

i. Yo _____ que las comidas del comedor son horribles.

j. Yo _____ en forma.

hago	es	libre	sigo	vapeo
creo	como	mañana	prefiero	estoy

3. Sentence puzzle: arrange the words in each sentence in the correct order.

a. como a yo sano menudo　　　　　　　　　[I often eat healthy meals]

_____

b. para sigo en estar una equilibrada forma dieta　　　[To stay fit, I have a balanced diet]

_____

c. estrés malo salud la para es el　　　　　　[Stress is bad for your health]

_____

d. salud la muy vapear es para malo　　　　　[Vaping is very bad for your health]

_____

e. yo ocho duermo noche cada al menos horas　　[I sleep at least eight hours per night]

_____

4. Complete the translations.

a. I vape: Yo vap_____　　　i. I avoid: Yo e_____

b. Bad: Ma_____　　　　　j. Heart: Co_____

c. Diet: Die_____　　　　　k. I sleep: Yo d_____

d. Health: Sa_____　　　　l. Often: A m_____

e. Healthy: Sa_____　　　　m. I think: Yo p_____

f. I eat: Yo co_____　　　　n. Balanced: Equil_____

g. Meal: La com_____　　　o. Vegetables: Ver_____

h. Unhealthy: No _____　　　p. I stay: Yo me q_____

5. Complete the table.

Infinitive	Present with *Yo*
Comer	Yo _____
Beber	
Tomar	
Evitar	
Hacer	
Ser	
Tener	

6. Complete the translation.

a. Para _____ en forma yo _____ ejercicio — [To stay fit I do sport]

b. En mi _____ podemos hacer _____ — [In my school we can do swimming]

c. La próxima _____ voy a montar en bicicleta — [Next week I am going to go cycling]

d. Para _____ más sano voy a hacerme _____ — [To be healthier I am going to become vegan]

e. _____ es malo para la _____ — [Vaping is bad for health]

f. Recientemente he _____ más _____ — [Recently I have eaten more vegetables]

g. Para _____ mi _____ hago más deporte — [To improve my fitness, I do more sport]

---

7. Translate into Spanish.

a. I like to eat chicken: M__ g_____ c_____ p_____ .

b. I like to drink coke: M__ g_____ b_____ Coca-Cola.

c. I go to the gym: V_____ a___ g_____ .

d. It is healthy: E___ s_____ .

e. Vaping is unhealthy: Va_____ n___ e___ s_____ .

f. I am fit: Y__ e_____ e__ f_____ .

g. I go swimming: V_____ a n_____ .

h I do sport: H_____ d_____ .

i. I sleep for eight hours: D_____ o_____ h_____ .

---

8. From present to past.

Present	Perfect Tense
Yo vapeo	Yo he vapeado
Yo juego	
Yo como	
Yo tomo	
Yo hago	
Yo nado	
Yo duermo	
Yo me levanto	

---

9. Complete with a suitable verb.

a. Para _____ en forma sigo una dieta sana.

b. _____ en bici.

c. Para mejorar mi forma física _____ comer menos dulces y chocolate.

d. Recientemente, he _____ de manera más saludable.

e. Normalmente _____ ocho horas cada noche.

f. Creo que _____ ___ hacerme vegana.

g. El fin de semana pasado _____ a la piscina.

h. Esta mañana he _____ un café y una magdalena.

i. Normalmente _____ con mis amigos.

j. _____ una buena salud.

k. _____ leyendo un libro.

l. No _____ suficiente ejercicio.

m. Me _____ a las once.

---

10. Translate into Spanish.

a. I like cycling and playing football with my friends.

b. It is important to follow a balanced diet.

c. In general, stress is bad for health.

d. You must try to do exercise every day.

e. I think I have a healthy diet.

f. I keep healthy by avoiding alcohol and drugs.

g. Next Sunday I'm going hiking in the countryside.

h. When I was younger, I used to eat too much sugar.

i. If I had more time I would play football every evening.

j. I have been at the pool with my friends.

k. Before eating, I did a bit of exercise.

Writing and speaking from a photo card

Describe the photo. Write about who you see, where they are and what they are doing. Read aloud and practise your description.

_____

_____

_____

_____

_____

_____

Answer the following questions related to this topic. Read out and practise your answers.

1. ¿Qué haces para mantenerte en forma?

   _____

2. ¿Qué deportes se pueden practicar en tu colegio?

   _____

3. ¿Qué comes para mantenerte sano?

   _____

4. ¿Qué opinas de los cigarrillos electrónicos o vapeadores?

   _____

5. ¿Qué vas a hacer el próximo fin de semana?

   _____

6. ¿Qué haces para relajarte?

   _____

7. ¿Qué comidas o productos sanos y no sanos has comido recientemente?

   _____

8. ¿Qué has hecho últimamente para mantenerte en forma?

   _____

   _____

9. ¿Qué piensas del veganismo?

   _____

10. ¿Qué vas a hacer esta tarde para evitar el estrés?

    _____

    _____

Speaking in a role-play

Look at the instructions on the left as they would appear in a speaking test. Read aloud with a partner the dialogue on the right. Then do the dialogue a second time, changing the answers in bold. Take turns playing the two roles.

Foundation (Where you see … your partner makes up a short answer as if they were an examiner).

1. Say what you eat to stay healthy (give one detail).
2. Say one thing you do to stay fit (give one detail).
3. Ask your friend a question about health.
4. Give one opinion about fast food.
5. Say what your favourite food dish is (give one detail).

1. ¿Qué comes para mantenerte sano? **Verduras.**
2. ¿Qué haces para estar en forma? **Juego al fútbol.**
3. ¿Haces algún deporte? …
4. ¿Qué opinas sobre la comida rápida? **No es saludable pero me gustan las hamburguesas.**
5. ¿Cuál es tu plato preferido? **La pasta.**

....

Higher (Where you see … your partner makes up a short answer as if they were an examiner).

1. Say what you do to stay healthy (give two details).
2. Say what you eat (give two details).
3. Ask your friend a question about health.
4. Give one opinion and one reason about school meals.
5. Describe a meal you ate recently (give two details).

1. ¿Qué haces para estar sano? **Como bien y hago deporte.**
2. ¿Cómo es tu dieta? **Como muchas verduras. Soy vegetariano/a.**
3. ¿Haces algún deporte? …
4. ¿Qué opinas sobre la comida del comedor? **Me gusta porque siempre hay mucha variedad.**
5. ¿Qué comiste ayer para la cena? **Anoche comí una pizza margarita y un postre delicioso.**

Foundation writing

Write approximately <u>50 words</u> in Spanish. Mention all points. Refer to the language in this unit, for example the Foundation Sentence Bank, or do the task in "exam conditions", without help. Or do both!

• What you like **to eat**   • What you like **to drink**   • **Sleep**   • What you do **to stay fit**   • What you do **to relax**

1. _____

2. _____

3. _____

4. _____

5. _____

Using your knowledge of grammar, complete the sentences below, choosing one of the three options given.

1 Por la tarde nosotros _____ al gimnasio (vamos/vais/va).

2 Mi hermano _____ al fútbol todos los días (juegan/juega/juegas).

3 El domingo pasado _____ (comí/he comido/comía) mucha fruta.

4 Me he comprado una bicicleta _____ (nuevo/nueva/nuevas).

5 Mi madre _____ mucho ejercicio esta semana (hace/hacía/ha hecho).

Foundation/Higher writing

Write approximately <u>90 words</u> in Spanish. You must refer to each bullet point.

• Vegetarianism.   • Something you did recently to stay healthy.   • What you will do to improve your health.

_____

_____

_____

_____

_____

_____

_____

_____

_____

_____

Higher writing

On paper, write approximately 150 words about positive lifestyle choices. Cover both bullet points. Refer to the language in this unit, for example the Higher Sentence Bank, or do the task in "exam conditions", without help. Or do both!

- The importance of having a healthy lifestyle.
- How you have changed your lifestyle choices in the past.

_____

_____

_____

_____

_____

_____

_____

_____

_____

_____

_____

_____

_____

_____

Foundation sentence bank

Hago mucho ejercicio porque es bueno para el corazón.	I do a lot of exercise because it's good for the heart.
Como frutas y verduras todos los días.	I eat fruit and vegetables each day.
Hago deporte a menudo en el colegio.	I do sport often at school.
A menudo como comida saludable.	I often eat healthy food.
Estoy en forma y saludable.	I am fit and healthy.
Duermo al menos ocho horas cada noche.	I sleep at least eight hours each night.
No fumo y evito vapear.	I don't smoke and I avoid vaping.
Para estar saludable, llevo una dieta equilibrada.	To stay healthy, I have a balanced diet.
No como mucho chocolate.	I don't eat a lot of chocolate.
Hice ciclismo y jugué al fútbol con mis amigos.	I did cycling and played football with my friends.
Voy a comer una dieta equilibrada.	I am going to eat a balanced diet.
En general, el estrés es malo para la salud.	In general, stress is bad for health.
Deberíamos intentar hacer ejercicio todos los días.	We should try to do exercise every day.
Creo que mi dieta es saludable.	I think my diet is healthy.

Higher sentence bank

Para mantenerme en forma hago deporte a menudo.	In order to stay fit I do sport often.
No consumo demasiada grasa.	I don't consume too much fat.
Mantengo mi salud evitando el alcohol y las drogas.	I keep healthy by avoiding alcohol and drugs.
Ayer para relajarme leí una novela toda la tarde.	Yesterday, to relax I read a novel all afternoon/evening.
Si tuviera más tiempo, haría yoga todas las noches.	If I had more time, I would do yoga each evening.
Me gustaría hacer más ejercicio, por ejemplo, correr.	I'd like to do more exercise, for example jogging.
Para llevar una vida saludable hay que dormir bien.	To lead a healthy life you have to sleep well.
Ayer después de comer fui al gimnasio.	Yesterday, after eating, I went to the gym.
El domingo que viene voy a ir de excursión al campo.	Next Sunday I'm going to go on a trip to the countryside.
Acabo de ir a la piscina con mis amigos.	I've just been to the pool with my friends.
Cuando era más joven, comía demasiada azúcar.	When I was younger, I used to eat too much sugar.
En el futuro quiero hacerme vegetariano.	In the future I want to become vegetarian.
Mi amiga es vegana desde hace seis meses.	My friend is vegan since six months ago.
Intento no comer demasiada carne roja.	I try not to eat too much red meat.

UNIT 2

Celebrity culture and entertainment

Contents

- Foundation vocab building.
- Foundation reading.
- Higher vocab building.
- Higher reading.
- Grammar focus – talking/writing about the future.
- Preparing for speaking and writing.
- Writing and speaking from a photo card.
- Speaking in a role play.
- Writing.
- Sentence bank.

Foundation vocab building

Vocabulary

el actor	actor (m)
la actriz	actor (f)
el autor	author (m)
la autora	author (f)
la boda	wedding
el cantante	singer
cantar	to sing
la carrera	degree
los medios de comunicación	media
cultural	cultural
el dinero	money
la entrevista	interview
el escritor	writer
escuchar	to listen
el equipo	team
el éxito	success
famoso	famous
el famoso	celebrity
el influencer	influencer
llevar	to wear
la moda	fashion
el modelo	model
el periódico	newspaper
la persona	person
el personaje	character
la política	politics
el programa	programme
rico	rich
seguir	to follow
telerrealidad	reality TV
el vídeo	video

1. Match.

Dinero	To sing
Programa	Interview
Cantante	Programme
Éxito	To wear
Entrevista	Career
Escritor	Money
Boda	Wedding
Llevar	Success
Carrera	Singer
Cantar	Writer

2. Complete.

a. F _ _ _ _ _ (celebrity) (f)

b. E _ _ _ _ _ _ (writer) (m)

c. I _ _ _ _ _ _ _ _ (influencer)

d. R _ _ _ (rich) (m)

e. B _ _ _ (wedding)

f. A _ _ _ _ (male actor)

g. A _ _ _ _ _ (female actor)

h. M _ _ _ (fashion)

i. P _ _ _ _ _ _ _ (programme)

j. C _ _ _ _ _ _ _ (singer)

3. Unjumble and translate into English as shown in the example.

a. ceriiópdo   periódico   *newspaper*

b. escchaur   _____ _____

c. sugier   _____ _____

d. odmoel   _____ _____

e. resictor   _____ _____

f. rracear   _____ _____

g. catrzi   _____ _____

h. eviod   _____ _____

i. pqueio   _____ _____

j. lalver   _____ _____

k. toaur   _____ _____

l. aelerelitdda   _____ _____

4. Fix any incorrect English translations.

a. Periódico: Journal

b. Cantante: Singer

c. Carrera: Car

d. Seguir: To wear

e. Escritora: Writer

f. Llevar: To follow

g. Equipo: Horse-riding

h. Dinero: Money

i. Escuchar: To admire

j. Programa: Personality

k. Entrevista: Interview

l. Cantar: To follow

5. Complete the translations.

a. Es un deportista famoso: He is a _____ sportsman.

b. Sigo a una influencer española en Instagram: I follow a Spanish _____ on Instagram.

c. Vi una buena entrevista con Salma Hayek: I saw a _____ interview with Salma Hayek.

d. Pienso que es una persona especial: I _____ he is a special person.

e. Es un personaje en una película de Marvel: He is a _____ in a Marvel film.

f. Es un político famoso: He is a famous _____.

g. Me encantan todas sus canciones: I love all his _____.

h. Mi cantante favorito es Pablo Alborán: My favourite _____ is Pablo Alborán.

6. Sentence puzzle: arrange the words below in the correct order.

a. favorita Es actriz es única mi porque   [She is my favourite actress because she is unique]

b. canciones encantan sus y Me estilo su   [I love her songs and her style]

c. un muy me películas bueno Es y encantan actor sus [He is a very good actor and I love his films]

d. Es por su película papel la Thor en famoso [He is famous for his role in the movie Thor]

e. a pasada su la Fui semana concierto   [I went to his/her concert last week]

f. rica Es modelo una y famosa   [She is a very famous and rich model]

g. gusta porque humilde es famoso, pero Me [I like him because he is famous but humble]

h. cine Es una del estrella   [He/she is a cinema star]

7. Circle the correct translation.

a. Entrevista	model	interview	singer
b. Moda	money	famous	fashion
c. Equipo	money	model	team
d. Bueno	good	bad	old
e. Seguir	to follow	to wear	to sing
f. Dinero	rich	money	funny
g. Famoso	silly	rich	famous
h. Cantante	speaker	singer	writer
i. Llevar	to sing	to wear	to cry
j. Actor	singer	actor	to sing
k. Con él	for him	with him	on him

8. Complete with the correct option from below.

a. Él _____ para el equipo de Real Madrid.

b. Ella es famosa por sus _____ de acción.

c. Ella canta una bonita _____.

d. Él es muy famoso y _____.

e. Es un actor y un _____ excelente.

f. Hace un _____ de superhéroe.

g. He _____ todas sus películas.

h. Ayer vi una entrevista con él en la _____.

películas	juega	canción	papel
tele	cantante	rico	visto

9. Translate into English.

a. Es un futbolista muy famoso. _____

b. Es una actriz y cantante excelente. _____

c. Vi una entrevista con él. ¡Fue genial! _____

d. Me encanta mucho su estilo y su carácter. _____

e. Ella es muy famosa por sus comedias románticas. _____

f. Fui a dos de sus conciertos. _____

g. Sigo a Taylor Swift en Instagram. _____

h. No sigo a los influencers en las redes sociales. _____

i. Es conocido por su papel en Star Wars. _____

j. Es una modelo famosa y rica. _____

k. Ha tenido una larga carrera deportiva. _____

l. Mis hermanos siguen a muchos influencers. _____

m. Mi escritora favorita es J.K. Rowling. _____

Foundation reading

1. **Read these comments about entertainment.**

Abel
Nunca voy al cine pero paso mucho tiempo viendo series por internet o en la tele.

Emilio
Para mí leer es lo más interesante. También escucho música en la radio.

Clara
Sigo a influencers en Instagram pero también me gusta ir al cine con mis amigos.

Who says what? Put a cross in the correct column for each question.

Who...	Abel	Emilio	Clara
a. ...likes to read?			
b. ...follows people online?			
c. ...goes to the cinema?			
d. ...listens to music?			
e. ...never goes to the cinema?			
f. ...watches series online?			

2. **Read this message from Karim to his friend Max.**

Hola, Max:

¿Has visto la nueva serie de Star Wars? A mí me gustó mucho: la historia es interesante y los actores son muy buenos. Sin embargo, es un poco larga.

También vi el domingo la nueva película de James Bond. Fue genial.

El fin de semana que viene voy a ver a mi cantante favorito en el teatro municipal.

Un abrazo,

Karim

Complete the gap in each sentence using a word from the box below. There are more words than gaps.

singer	film	long	boring
Sunday	Saturday	actor	

a. Karim thought the Star Wars series was _____.

b. On _____ he saw the latest Bond movie.

c. Next weekend he'll see his favourite _____.

Foundation reading

3. **Read what these four people say about their favourite Spanish-speaking actors.**

> **Miriam**
> Me encanta Gael García Bernal por su personalidad. Actuó en la película "Amores perros" y en la serie "Mozart in the Jungle". Es guapo y simpático.
>
> **Javier**
> Mi actriz favorita es Úrsula Corberó. Es delgada y morena. Actuó en una famosa serie criminal, "La casa de papel", y en una película de superhéroes, "Snake Eyes".
>
> **Manu**
> Mi actor preferido es Pedro Pascal. Es divertido y tiene bigote. Me encantó su actuación en "The Last of Us", incluso si es una serie en inglés. Ganó varios premios por ese papel.
>
> **Sara**
> Siempre me ha gustado Salma Hayek. Tiene una larga carrera en cine y televisión. No es muy alta y tiene el pelo negro.

Who says…? Put a cross in the correct box.

Who says that their favourite actor…	Miriam	Javier	Manu	Sara
a. …is friendly?				
b. …has had a long career?				
c. …was in a crime series?				
d. …was in a superheroes film?				
e. …has dark hair?				
f. …won awards for a film?				

4. **Read what Eduardo has to say about celebrity culture, then answer the questions in English.**

> Me gusta leer sobre gente famosa porque me parece muy interesante. También me encantan las fotos de celebridades porque me interesa la moda.
> Mi amiga Sofía dice que los famosos a veces hablan de sus problemas de salud mental y creo que eso es bueno.
> Mi amigo Samir dice que algunos famosos son buenos explicando temas sociales a los adolescentes, como la pobreza en el mundo.

a. Why does Eduardo like to read articles about celebrities?

_____

b. Why does he like photos of celebrities?

_____

c. According to Sofía, what do stars sometimes talk about?

_____

d. According to Samir, what do some celebrities talk about?

_____

Foundation reading

5. **Read what these people think about celebrity culture.**

Lisa
Es muy divertido seguir la vida de mis actores y actrices favoritos. Me inspiran mucho.

Mateo
Me parece aburrido y poco interesante. ¿Por qué interesarse por la vida de los demás cuando uno tiene su propia vida que vivir?

Valentina
No me interesa la vida de los ricos y famosos. Creo que hay cosas más importantes en la vida.

Alejandro
Miro mis redes sociales todos los días. Me gusta mucho seguir a influencers

Aitana
Me gusta leer sobre gente famosa pero creo que a veces paso demasiado tiempo haciéndolo *(doing it)*.

If the person has a positive opinion put P in the box. If they have a negative opinion put N in the box. If they express both a positive and negative opinion put P/N in the box.

Lisa [ ]   Mateo [ ]   Valentina [ ]   Alejandro [ ]   Aitana [ ]

6. **Three people are giving their opinion about the Spanish singer Rosalía. Complete the sentences below the box.**

Carla

Es una cantante increíble con una gran voz. Además, las letras de sus canciones son muy interesantes. Me encantó su primer álbum.

Pablo

Creo que es popular porque la gente puede identificarse con sus experiencias personales. A mí me encanta.

Martina

Paso mucho tiempo escuchando su música. Prefiero su segundo álbum, que salió el año pasado.

---

a. Carla thinks Rosalía is an amazing _____ with a great _____ She loved her _____ album.

b. Pablo thinks that she is popular because people can _____ with her personal experiences.

c. Martina _____ of time listening to her music. She prefers her _____ album from last year.

Higher vocab building

Vocabulary

el aficionado	*fan*
el anuncio	*advertisment*
de moda	*fashionable*
dirigir	*to direct*
la gira	*tour*
estar inspirado	*to be inspired*
el/la influencer	*influencer*
la letra	*lyrics*
la marca	*brand*
las noticias	*the news*
la novela	*novel*
orgulloso	*proud*
el papel	*role*
el periódico	*newspaper*
el papel	*the role*
el pasatiempo	*the hobby*
el pasatiempo	*the hobby*
el premio	*prize*
el público	*the audience*
presentar	*to present*
publicar	*to publish*
quedar	*to arrange, to meet*
reconocer	*to recognise*
red/redes	*network(s)*
la riqueza	*wealth*
la ropa	*clothes*
seguir	*to follow*
la serie	*the series*
el tatuaje	*the tattoo*
el teatro	*theatre*
la telenovela	*the soap opera*
triste	*sad*
la víctima	*victim*
la voz	*voice*

1. Compare the English words below with their Spanish equivalent and underline the differences in the Spanish word.

Español	English	Español	English
Anunciar	To announce	Víctima	Victim
Elegante	Elegant	Heroína	Heroine
Premio	Prize	Personaje	Character
Héroe	Hero	Famoso	Famous
Publicar	To publish	Teatro	Theatre
Novela	Novel	Publicidad	Publicity
Escándalo	Scandal	Presentar	To present
Voz	Voice	Persona	Person

2. Match up.

Red	To follow
Periódico	Novel
Novela	Proud
Seguir	To publish
Orgulloso/a	Brand
Publicar	Network
Marca	Voice
Voz	Newspaper

3. Complete and translate.

a. Pu _ _ _ _ _ _: _____

b. Pode _ _ _ _: _____

c. R _ _ _ _: _____

d. Se _ _ _ _: _____

e. G _ _ _: _____

f. Pr _ _ _ _: _____

g. Ma _ _ _: _____

4. Translate into English.

a. Rosalía tiene una gran voz. _____

b. Pablo Alborán visita muchas ciudades durante sus giras.

_____

c. Ha sido víctima de un ataque. _____

d. Las letras de sus canciones son muy bonitas

_____

5. Sentence puzzle: arrange the words in each sentence in the right order.

a. su voz Me encanta es muy potente porque [I love his voice because it is very powerful].

_____

b. sociales La redes las en sigo [I follow her on social networks].

_____

c. está de gira Ella en Europa [She is on a tour of Europe].

_____

d. Me inspiran su y él personaje [I am inspired by him and his character].

_____

6. Anagrams.

a. zov: _____

b. aigr: _____

c. rerpsetna: _____

d. ogrlloous: _____

e. onunaic: _____

f. nrecocero: _____

g. lppae: _____

h. armidra: _____

i. pora: _____

j. aarmc : _____

7. Complete with the correct option.

a. Me gusta mucho su voz porque es _____.

b. Yo sigo a Blanca Suárez en las _____ sociales.

c. Ella está de _____ en Estados Unidos ahora mismo.

d. Fui a un _____ suyo durante su gira por Italia.

e. Ella siempre _____ ropa muy guay.

f. Me _____ a ser una persona mejor.

g. Él sale en muchas _____.

h. Él ha hecho muchas películas _____.

lleva	potente	películas	buenas
gira	concierto	redes	inspira

8. Fix the incorrect translations below.

a. Admirar: To watch _____

b. Quedar: To announce _____

c. Orgulloso: Mean _____

d. La heroína: Character _____

e. El periódico: The day _____

f. La marca: Tour _____

g. La apertura: Network _____

h. La letra: Songs _____

i. El anuncio: Wealth _____

9. Translate into English.

a. Una estrella de la moda: _____

b. Una mujer muy orgullosa: _____

c. Una nueva marca: _____

d. Unas letras interesantes: _____

e. Unos anuncios divertidos: _____

f. Un papel importante: _____

g. Él publicó una nueva novela: _____

h. La inauguración de un teatro: _____

i. Ganar un premio importante: _____

10. Translate into English.

a. Es mi autor preferido. Escribe novelas muy buenas.

_____

b. Es mi cantante favorita. Tiene una voz potente y me encantan las letras de sus canciones.

_____

c. Yo la admiro porque tiene mucho talento y además, tiene una voz preciosa.

_____

d. Lo que más me gusta es que, aunque es rica y famosa, es muy humilde.

_____

e. No sigo a influencers como él en internet porque dicen muchas tonterías *(silly things)*.

_____

f. Después de ver su última serie le seguí en Instagram.

_____

Higher reading

1. Read this article about problems in stars' lives.

> El principal problema es que no tienen intimidad. Por eso, algunos aeropuertos importantes tienen un servicio VIP para famosos. Hay una terminal secreta para famosos donde se puede contratar seguridad para pasar sin ser reconocido.
>
> Además, los famosos casi nunca utilizan el transporte público. Prefieren viajar en taxi o limusina.
>
> Por último, para evitar ser reconocidos, las celebridades cambian frecuentemente de número de teléfono y se comunican entre ellos a través de sus agentes. A menudo tienen cuentas* privadas y secretas en Instagram y X.
>
> * Cuenta = Account

What does the article say? Put a tick next to each one of THREE statements made in the article.

a. Stars have no private life.

b. Stars avoid taking taxis.

c. Stars don't use public transport.

d. Stars keep their phone number secret.

e. Some airports have a special terminal for celebrities.

f. Stars communicate with their agents by phone.

2. Read this article about Spanish swim champion Mireia Belmonte. Then answer the questions in English.

> Mireia Belmonte, nacida el 10 de noviembre de 1990 en Badalona, es una famosa nadadora. A lo largo de su carrera, ha sido siete veces campeona mundial en piscina corta. Fue campeona olímpica en Londres 2012, donde ganó dos medallas de plata, y Río de Janeiro 2016, donde ganó una medalla de oro y una de bronce. También ha ganado cuatro veces el campeonato de Europa en piscina larga y nueve veces en piscina corta.
>
> Por último, ella fue, junto el piragüista Saúl Craviotto, la abanderada española en los Juegos Olímpicos de Tokio 2020. Aunque no ganó ninguna medalla en esa competición, es la nadadora española con más premios de la historia.
>
> Con respecto a su vida privada, Mireia estudia un Grado en Publicidad y Relaciones Públicas, tiene un perro llamado London y le encanta la moda.

a. What did she win in 2012? _____

b. What exactly did she win in Rio de Janeiro? _____

c. How would you translate "abanderada"? _____

d. Why is Saúl Craviotto mentioned? _____

e. What do we learn about her private life? _____

Higher reading

3. **Read this account by Vega of a concert and answer the questions below in English.**

Soy una gran fan de la música electrónica, así que cuando me enteré de que mi grupo favorito, Delaporte, venía a Valencia, compré una entrada seis meses antes del concierto. Invité a mi mejor amiga Natalia a venir conmigo, porque a ella también le encanta el grupo.

Cogimos el tren a Valencia y luego el metro hasta el estadio donde se celebraba el concierto. Estaba muy contenta, porque cantaron mi canción favorita, "Un jardín". Tocaron todos sus grandes éxitos. Bailamos y cantamos con ellos. Fue una noche que nunca olvidaremos, y nos alegramos mucho de haber vivido esa experiencia.

He visto entrevistas con la cantante, Sandra Delaporte. Creo que es simpática y que sus letras son interesantes, por ejemplo cuando habla de salud mental.

a. When did Vega buy her ticket? _____

b. Translate into English the title of her favourite song. _____

c. How does she describe the whole evening? _____

d. What does she find interesting about the lead singer? _____

e. What example does she give at the end? _____

4. **Read this review by Juan of a Argentinian film called "Argentina 1985", then circle the best option in each case.**

El domingo pasado vi por segunda vez esta película en internet. Trata sobre un juicio a varios militares que lideraron la dictadura militar de Argentina de los años 70 y 80. Lo que más me gusta es su realismo y la calidad de las interpretaciones. Por supuesto, la película nos recuerda la violencia de la dictadura y los problemas que existieron después durante los primeros años de democracia. Estos sucesos sucedieron hace más de cuarenta años pero algunos de los temas continúan siendo relevantes hoy.

1. Juan saw the film: (a) on TV (b) at the cinema (c) online

2. Juan finds the film: (a) well-acted (b) unbelievable (c) old-fashioned

3. According to Juan , the film depicts: (a) love (b) poverty (c) violence

4. Juan finds the movie: (a) moving (b) important (c) relevant

Higher reading

5. Read this article about a popular online creator from Spain. Answer the questions in English.

> Carla Llamas es una periodista de viajes española que tiene casi un millón de seguidores en TikTok e Instagram. Además, tiene un blog de viajes muy popular que creó en 2011 y un podcast.
>
> Carla crea contenido sobre sus viajes alrededor del mundo, como su viaje a Argentina en diciembre de 2023. Ella también publica mucho sobre viajar con niños porque tiene una hija pequeña con su pareja, Adrián. Asimismo, escribe a menudo sobre turismo responsable con el medioambiente.
>
> Carla ha colaborado con varias marcas que utiliza en su día a día, incluyendo una dedicada a la creación de álbumes fotográficos. Finalmente, es cofundadora junto con otras influencers de viaje de un festival diseñado específicamente para madres viajeras.

a. In what platforms does she work?

_____

b. What type of content does Carla share?

_____

c. What happened in December 2023?

_____

d. What do we learn about her private life? Mention two details.

_____

e. What did she co-create and who is it aimed at?

_____

6. Read this review of a Mexican TV series. Then tick the best option in each case.

> *"Horario estelar"* es una serie de suspense de 2023. Filmada en distintas partes de México, la serie se sitúa en la actualidad y narra la historia de un famoso presentador de televisión que informa sobre un caso de homicidio en el que está involucrado *(involved)* aunque nadie lo sabe. La víctima es su amante. Desde su programa de televisión, el presentador intenta manipular la investigación de un caso en el que todos los personajes están conectados.
>
> La primera temporada tiene diez capítulos que reflexionan sobre la doble moral de los medios de comunicación y la situación de seguridad en México. Es una serie apasionante pero los espectadores no siempre pueden generar empatía con los personajes. Esto debe mejorar en la segunda temporada.

	a.	b.	c.
1. The TV series is:	old	based on a novel	about a TV presenter.
2. The TV series takes place in:	one part of Mexico	different parts of Mexico	two different parts of Mexico
3. The first ten episodes are about:	morality of the media	security in the media	wealth of the media
4. The series was:	original	thrilling	empathic

Grammar focus
Talking or writing about the future

Read the sentences below.

*Mañana **veo** una película con mi amiga.*　　Tomorrow **I watch** a film with my friend.
*Mañana **voy a ver** una película con mi amiga.*　　Tomorrow **I am going to watch** a film with my friend.
*Mañana **veré** una película con mi amiga.*　　Tomorrow **I will watch** a film with my friend.

You can see that to express future events we can usually use three different verb forms. The same is true in English.

PRESENT	NEAR FUTURE	FUTURE SIMPLE TENSE
Yo veo (I watch)	Yo voy a ver (I am going to watch)	Yo veré (I will watch)

We use the present tense when we talk about a future that is certain, same as in English. In general, think what verb form you'd use in English and it will usually be the same in Spanish.

In the exam, you will sometimes be asked to speak or write about future events. Very often, the present tense will be fine, but if you show you can vary your language by using the near future or future tense there are some extra marks to be gained.

In the grid below, mark whether the event described is in the **past, present** or **future**, as in the example. Look for other clues in the sentence, apart from the verb. Then translate the sentence.

Ejemplo: Anoche vi una película.	PAST	Yesterday I watched a film.
a. Mañana voy al cine.		
b. Miro mi Instagram todos los días.		
c. Escucho a mi cantante preferido.		
d. El fin de semana que viene voy a un concierto.		
e. Voy a ver una película de mi actriz favorita en el cine.		
f. Veré mi serie preferida.		
g. Voy a ir a un concierto: ¡va a ser genial!		
h. Fui a ver un espectáculo en el teatro.		
i. Subo vídeos a Snapchat casi todos los días.		
j. Mi madre va a escuchar su disco favorito.		
k. Hemos visto a una persona famosa.		
l. Mañana vamos a ver Netflix.		
m. He visto la nueva película de James Bond.		
n. Sigo a mi actor preferido en X.		

The Near Future

Time marker	Present of IR	Preposition 'a'	Infinitive of verb
Hoy (today)	Yo **voy** (I am going)	**a** (to)	**anunciar** (to announce)
Esta mañana (this morning)	Tú **vas** (you are going)		**cambiar** (to change)
Esta tarde (this afternoon/evening)	Él/ella **va** (he/she is going)		**comprar** (to buy)
Esta noche (tonight)	Usted **va** (you formal singular are going)		**escuchar** (to listen)
Mañana (tomorrow)			**ir** (to go)
El año que viene (next year)	Nosotros **vamos** (we are going)		**jugar** (to play)
La semana que viene (next week)	Vosotros **vais** (you are going)		**leer** (to read)
El mes que viene (next month)			**llevar** (to wear)
	Ellos/ellas **van** (they are going)		**mirar** (to see)
El fin de semana que viene (next weekend)			**publicar** (to publish)
	Ustedes **van** (you formal plural are going)		**salir** (to go out)
			seguir (to follow)
			subir (to upload)
			ver (to see, watch)

1. Match up.

Seguir	To go
Anunciar	To wear
Ir	To follow
Llevar	To buy
Salir	To win
Ganar	To announce
Comprar	To see
Mirar	To go out
Ver	To read
Leer	To listen
Publicar	To upload
Subir	To watch
Escuchar	To publish

2. Complete with the correct form of "Ir."

a. Mañana ella _____ a sacar una nueva canción.

b. En la gala ustedes _____ a llevar ropa muy elegante.

c. Esta noche nosotros _____ a ir a un concierto.

d. Este fin de semana yo _____ a leer su última novela.

e. Sergio Ramos _____ a ganar el Balón de Oro.

f. Nosotros _____ a comprar zapatos de marca.

g. Ellas _____ a cortarse el pelo este fin de semana.

h. ¿ _____ (tú) a ver su última película esta tarde?

i. Usted _____ a subir fotos de su boda a Instagram.

j. ¿Vosotros _____ a ver la nueva serie en la tele?

3. Complete with the missing letters.

a. Yo v_ _ a comp_ _ _
(I am going to buy)

b. Nosotros v_ _ _ _ a cam_ _ _ _
(We are going to change)

c. Ellos v_ _ a seg _ _ _
(They are going to follow)

d. Ella v_ a sa_ _ _
(She is going to go out)

e. Vosotros v_ _ _ a v_ _
(You guys are going to see)

4. Translate.

a. We are going to change our car today.

b. He is going to win an award for his latest movie.

c. I am going to follow Ariana Grande on Instagram.

d. She is going to publish her photos on social media.

e. They (f) are going to go to her concert tomorrow.

f. He is going to announce his wedding this evening.

g. Are you going to watch his programme today?

h. This afternoon I am going to listen to his songs.

The Simple Future

Regular verbs

Ganar – *to win*	Ver – *to see*	Subir – *to upload*
Yo ganar**é**	Yo ver**é**	Yo subir**é**
Tú ganar**ás**	Tú ver**ás**	Tú subir**ás**
Él/ella/usted ganar**á**	Él/ella/usted ver**á**	Él/ella/usted subir**á**
Nosotros ganar**emos**	Nosotros ver**emos**	Nosotros subir**emos**
Vosotros ganar**éis**	Vosotros ver**éis**	Vosotros subir**éis**
Ellos/ustedes ganar**án**	Ellos/ustedes ver**án**	Ellos/ustedes subir**án**

Irregular verbs (verbs with irregular stems)

Hacer *to do*	Yo har**é** … *I will do*	**Decir** *to say*	Yo dir**é** … *I will say*
Poder *to be able to*	Yo podr**é** … *I will be able to*	**Querer** *to want*	Yo querr**é** … *I will want*
Salir *to go out*	Yo saldr**é** … *I will go out*	**Tener** *to have*	Yo tendr**é** … *I will have*

---

5. Choose the correct verb ending.

a. Yo ver**é/ás/á** su última película.

b. Ella ir**é/ás/á** al concierto de Aitana.

c. Nosotros le esperar**emos/éis/án** delante del club.

d. Ellos publicar**emos/áis/án** su novela muy pronto.

e. Usted publicar**é/ás/á** su nuevo disco mañana.

f. Vosotros la seguir**emos/éis/án** en su gira.

---

6. Complete with the correct ending.

a. Ella ver_   g. Vosotros ir_ _ _

b. Nosotros ser_ _ _ _   h. Él ir_

c. Yo escuchar _   i. Ellos ganar _ _

d. Usted anunciar_   j. Vosotros estar_ _ _

e. Ellos har_ _   k. Tú leer_ _

f. Tú comprar_ _   l. Yo anunciar _

---

7. Complete the table.

Infinitivo	Presente	Futuro simple
Hacer	Yo hago	Yo haré
Publicar		
Salir		
Escuchar		
Comprar		
Ser		
Tener		
Asistir		
Mirar		
Ver		

---

8. Complete.

a. Yo te _____ (I will wait for you)

b. Nosotros le _____ (We will follow him)

c. Ustedes lo _____ (You, plural, formal will announce it)

d. ¿Tú lo _____? (Will you watch it?)

e. Ellos te_____ (They will listen to you)

f. Nosotros lo_____ (We will buy it)

g. Ella lo _____ (She will win it)

h. Yo los _____ (I will buy them)

---

9. Translate into Spanish.

a. I will wait for his new album.

b. He will win an award.

c. We will buy her new perfume.

d. She will be more famous.

e. Next year she will publish a new novel.

f. They will announce their marriage soon.

g. I will listen to her new song.

h. We will wait for her at the entrance of the stadium.

i. She will be a celebrity very soon.

j. This evening they will watch his latest series.

k. I will follow her on social media.

l. Next week we will go to his concert in Valencia.

Preparing for speaking and writing

1. Complete the table.

English	Spanish
Fashion	La m _ _ _
Programme	El p_ _ _ _ _ _
I watched	Yo _ _
Hobby	El p_ _ _ _ _ _ _ _
Celebrity	El f_ _ _ _ _
Recently	R_ _ _ _ _ _ _ _ _ _
Favourite	F_ _ _ _ _ _
Advantage	V_ _ _ _ _ _
Famous	F_ _ _ _ _
Lyrics	L_ _ _ _

2. Complete with the correct option.

a. Penélope Cruz es mi actriz _____.

b. Él se _____ Roberto.

c. Ella es una _____ muy famosa.

d. Yo _____ que este programa es genial.

e. No me gustan las _____ sociales.

f. La semana que viene yo _____ a ir a un concierto.

g. Mi _____ favorito es jugar al fútbol.

h. Me encantan las letras de sus _____.

canciones	llama	favorita	pasatiempo
redes	voy	creo	cantante

3. Gapped translation.

a. La semana _____ voy a _____ al cine. [Next week I am going to go to the cinema]

b. ___ canción _____ es "Solamente tú" de Pablo Alborán. [My favourite song is ´Solamente tú´ by Pablo Alborán]

c. Taylor Swift es _____, delgada y _____. [Taylor Swift is tall, slim, and beautiful]

d. Este fin de semana _____ una película en el _____. [This weekend I will see a film in the cinema]

e. El _____ acaba de sacar una _____ canción. [This singer has just released a new song]

f. Me encantan los _____ de música y de _____. [I love music and fashion programmes]

g. _____ voy a _____ un partido de fútbol. [Tomorrow I am going to watch a football match]

4. Complete.

a. Mo_ _ (fashion)

b. Pr_ _ _ _ (award)

c. Gi _ _ (tour)

d. Mar_ _ (brand)

e. Act_ _ (male actor)

f. Fam_ _ _ (male celebrity)

g. Or_ _ _ _ _ _ (proud)

h. Can _ _ _ _ (song)

i. Pr _ _ _ _ _ _ (to prefer)

j. P_ _ _ _ (role)

k. Act_ _ _ (actress)

l. Las noti _ _ _ _(TV news)

m. Pro _ _ _ _ _ (programme)

n. V_ _ (to see)

o. Ca_ _ _ _ _ _ (singer)

p. G _ _ _ _ _ (to like)

q. Com _ _ _ _ (comedy)

r. Escr _ _ _ _ (writer)

5. Add the missing accents.

a. Mi pelicula favorita es "Lo imposible".

b. Hoy no hay programas sobre futbol en la tele.

c. Odio las novelas de ciencia ficcion.

d. Hemos subido un video a Snapchat.

e. Ella no sera famosa en el futuro.

f. El no tiene vida privada.

g. Yo veo series de television.

h. Yo prefiero su ultima cancion.

i. Luego subire unas fotos a Instagram.

6. Complete with a suitable verb in the right tense.

a. Mi pasatiempo favorito _____ la natación.   (present)

b. Mi famoso preferido _____ Lionel Messi.   (present)

c. Yo _____ a menudo al cine.   (present)

d. Mañana nosotros _____ una comedia romántica.   (near future)

e. Yo no _____ jamás famoso/a.   (future)

f. Lo que más me _____ de él es su talento.   (present)

g. Esta noche _____ una película de acción.   (near future)

h. Me encanta _____ las canciones de Shakira.   (infinitive)

7. Translate into Spanish.

a. Funny (f):   G_____

b. Tall (m):   A_____

c. Thin (m):   D_____

d. Good-looking (f): G_____

e. Proud (f):   O_____

f. Silly (m):   T_____

g. Famous (f):   F_____

h. Rich (m):   R_____

i. Good (f):   B_____

8. Translate into Spanish (easier).

a. He is rich.   _____

b. She is famous.   _____

c. I respect him.   _____

d. I admire her.   _____

e. I listen to her songs.   _____

f. I like the lyrics.   _____

g. I am inspired by her.   _____

h. She is very proud.   _____

i. I watch her movies.   _____

j. He is a super-hero.   _____

k. I love fashion.   _____

l. She is a star.   _____

m. He is rich and famous.   _____

n. He plays football.   _____

o. She has a good voice.   _____

p. I love his clothes.   _____

9. Translate into Spanish (harder).

a. I admire her for her great talent.   _____

b. What I like most is her powerful voice.   _____

c. It's the best novel I have read.   _____

d. I've just been to a concert of my favourite group.   _____

e. After watching the film, I followed him on Insta.   _____

f. It's the lyrics of the songs that I like most.   _____

g. Next Monday I'm going to go and see her.   _____

h. In my opinion, she's an extraordinary actress.   _____

i. He has published many novels that I love.   _____

j. Two years ago, I saw her on stage in London.   _____

k. Many young people follow the celebrities.   _____

l. We're going to go out. It will be great!   _____

m. I shall watch my favourite programme on YouTube.   _____

n. Her powerful voice inspires me.   _____

Writing and speaking from a photo card

Write something about both of these photos. Write about who you see, where they are what they are doing. Read out your description.

_____

_____

_____

_____

_____

_____

Answer the following questions related to this topic. Read out your answers.

1. ¿Cuál es tu famoso favorito? Descríbelo.

   _____

   _____

2. ¿Qué tipos de programas de televisión te gustan?

   _____

3. Escribe sobre una película que has visto recientemente.

   _____

   _____

   _____

4. ¿Qué pasatiempos tienes?

   _____

   _____

5. ¿Qué vas a hacer el fin de semana que viene?

   _____

   _____

   _____

Speaking in a role-play

Look at the instructions on the left as they would appear in a speaking test. Read aloud with a partner the dialogue on the right. Then do the dialogue a second time, changing the answers in bold. Take turns playing the two roles.

Foundation

1. Mention one programme you watch on TV or online.	1. ¿Qué programa ves en la tele o en internet? **Doctor Who.**
2. Give one opinion about this programme.	2. ¿Cuál es tu opinión sobre este programa? **Me encanta Doctor Who.**
3. Ask your friend a question about films.	3. ¿Te gusta ver películas? ...
4. Describe your favourite actor (give one detail).	4. Háblame de tu actor favorito. **Se llama Óscar Isaac.**
5. Say what you do at the weekend (give one detail).	5. ¿Qué haces los fines de semana? **Juego al rugby**

....

Higher (Where you see ...., the partner makes up a short answer as if they were an examiner).

1. Describe a celebrity you like (give two details).	1. ¿A quién admiras? **Admiro a Rozalén. Es una cantante española.**
2. Say if you would like to be famous in the future and why / why not (give one opinion and one reason).	2. ¿Te gustaría ser famoso en el futuro? **No me gustaría ser famoso porque no tendría vida privada.**
3. Ask your friend a question about fame.	3. ¿Crees que es importante ser famoso ? ...
4. Give one advantage and one disadvantage of social media.	4. ¿Qué piensas de las redes sociales? **Están bien para tener una vida social activa pero paso demasiado tiempo en línea.**
5. Say something about reality TV (give one detail).	5. ¿Qué opinas sobre los programas de telerrealidad? **Me parecen muy aburridos.**

Foundation writing

Write about 50 words in Spanish. Write something about each point.

• A favourite celebrity • What they look like • Their character • What they do • Why you respect them

1. _____

2. _____

3. _____

4. _____

5. _____

Using your knowledge of grammar complete the sentences below, choosing one of the three options given.

1. Yo _____ al cine a menudo (vamos/voy/va).

2. Nosotros _____ series en la televisión (vemos/ves/ve).

3. El domingo pasado yo _____ a mi actriz favorita (visteis/vi/viste).

4. Mi cantante preferido ha sacado una canción _____ (nueva/nuevo/nuevas).

5. Ahora mi madre regularmente _____ mucho deporte (hace/hizo/ha hecho).

Foundation/Higher writing

Write approximately 90 words in Spanish. You must refer to each bullet point.

• Types of film and series you like • What you saw recently on TV • What you will watch in the future

_____

_____

_____

_____

_____

_____

_____

Higher writing

In your exercise book or on paper, write approximately 150 words about celebrity culture. You must write something about both bullet points. You can either refer to the language in this unit, for example the sentence bank, or do the task in "exam conditions", without help. Or you could do both!

• The positive and negative aspects of being a celebrity
• When you watched a favourite celebrity recently

Foundation sentence bank

Mi actriz favorita es Blanca Suárez.	My favourite actress is Blanca Suárez.
Antonio Banderas es un buen modelo a seguir.	Antonio Banderas is a good role model.
Me gusta porque es un buen actor.	I like him because he's a good actor.
He visto una buena película en el cine.	I watched a good film at the cinema.
Yo voy al cine de vez en cuando.	I go to the cinema occasionally.
Yo voy a ir a un concierto con mis amigos.	I'm going to go to a gig with my friends.
Creo que ella es una persona muy especial.	I think that she's a very special person.
Mi autora favorita es J. K. Rowling.	My favourite author is J.K.Rowling.
Yo voy a ver un programa de televisión.	I'm going to watch a programme on TV.
Me gusta ver a influencers en YouTube.	I like to watch influencers on YouTube.
Para mí, la moda no es importante.	For me, fashion is not important.
Mi cantante favorita es Tini.	My favourite singer is Tini.
Es una personalidad deportiva famosa.	He/she is a famous sports personality.
Yo he visto una buena entrevista con él/ella.	I saw a good interview with him/her.

Higher sentence bank

Yo lo admiro por su gran talento.	I admire him for his great talent.
Lo que más me gusta de él es su poderosa voz.	What I like most is his powerful voice.
Es la mejor novela que he leído	It's the best novel I have read.
Acabo de estar en un concierto de mi grupo favorito.	I've just been to a gig by my favourite group.
Después de ver la série, empecé a seguir al actor en Instagram	After watching the series, I started following the actor on Insta.
Son las letras de las canciones lo que más me gusta.	It's the lyrics of the songs that I like most.
El lunes que viene voy a ir a verla en un concierto.	Next Monday I'm going to see her on tour.
Yo no sigo a ningún influencer.	I don't follow a single influencer online.
Él ha publicado muchas novelas que me encantan.	He has published many novels that I love.
Me relajo leyendo artículos sobre series.	I relax by reading articles about series.
Hace dos años la vi en el escenario en Londres.	Two years ago I saw her on stage in London.
Los famosos son modelos a seguir para los jóvenes.	Celebrities are role models for young people.
Nunca soy influenciada por los famosos.	I am never influenced by celebrities.
Odio los programas de telerrealidad.	I hate reality TV programmes.

UNIT 3

Environment

Contents

- Foundation vocab building.
- Foundation reading.
- Higher vocab building.
- Higher reading.
- Grammar focus – using the Conditional.
- Preparing for speaking and writing.
- Writing and speaking from a photo card.
- Speaking in a role play.
- Writing.
- Sentence bank.

Foundation vocab building

Vocabulary

el agua	water
amenazar	to threaten
la basura	rubbish/waste
el bosque	forest
cambio climático	climate change
caliente	hot
el campo	countryside
el cielo	sky
construir	to build
contaminar	to pollute
la costa	coast
destruir	to destroy
debemos	we must
estar situado	to be located
la fábrica	factory
fabricar	to manufacture
la falta de	the lack of
frío	cold
la geografía	geography
la granja	farm
grave/serio	serious
el hambre	hunger
el invierno	winter
limpio	clean
la isla	island
el lugar	place
la luz	light
el mar	sea
el medioambiente	environment
la muerte	death
el mundo	world
el papel	paper
el paro	unemployment
el peligro	danger
el planeta	planet
el plástico	plastic
la playa	beach
la pobreza	poverty
reciclar	to recycle
reducir	to reduce
el ruido	noise
el sol	sun
tirar	to throw (away)
la Tierra	Earth
usar	to use
el verano	summer
el viento	wind
vivir	to live

1. Match up.

Ruido	Cold
Sol	Hot
Reciclar	Waste
Agua	Noise
Frío	Hunger
Basura	Recycling
Calor	Factories
Hambre	Farm
Fábricas	Sun
Granja	Coast
Costa	Water

2. Correct the wrong translations.

a. Guapo: Ugly

b. En verano: In the winter.

c. El cielo es azul: The water is blue.

d. Mucho ruido: A lot of rubbish.

e. Hace frío: It is hot.

f. En la costa: In the countryside.

g. El bosque: The boss key.

h. El calentamiento: Recycling.

3. One of three – circle the right answer.

Sol	cold	sun	heat
Basura	waste	hunger	thirst
Falta	lack	island	world
Mundo	water	world	wind
Tirar	to destroy	to build	to throw
Ruido	light	bin	noise
Tierra	winter	Earth	island
Fábrica	factory	square	town
Vivir	to earn	to die	to live
Lugar	lack	place	light

4. Tick the verbs with a negative meaning.

a. Destruir.

b. Amenazar.

c. Construir.

d. Fabricar.

e. Contaminar.

f. Mejorar.

g. Vivir.

h. Matar.

i. Reciclar.

5. Complete the translation.

a. El calentamiento global: Global _____

b. Hace sol: It is _____

c. El reciclaje de basura: The recycling of _____

d. La contaminación de las aguas: The pollution of _____

e. Las fábricas contaminan el mar: Factories pollute the _____

f. No hay suficientes cubos de basura: There are not enough _____

6. Translate into English.

a. Fábrica _____

b. Viento _____

c. Vivir _____

d. La falta de _____

e. Peligro _____

f. Mundo _____

g. Luz _____

h. Playa _____

i. Mar _____

j. Propio _____

k. Invierno _____

l. Amenaza _____

7. Sentence puzzle – put the words in each sentence in the right order

a. hay En mucha contaminación mi pueblo   [In my town there is a lot of pollution]

_____

b. reducir Es necesario de la cantidad basura   [It is necessary to reduce the amount of rubbish]

_____

c. en las calles No hay cubos suficientes de basura   [There aren't enough rubbish bins on the streets]

_____

d. aumentando Las temperaturas están verano cada   [The temperatures are rising every summer]

_____

e. de los bosques Lo que es destrucción la me preocupa   [What worries me is the destruction of the forests]

_____

f. del país en bonito un pueblo Yo en vivo el sur   [I live in a pretty town in the south of the country]

_____

g. naturales es La falta recursos de preocupante   [The lack of natural resources is worrying]

_____

8. Translate into English.

a. El reciclaje de la basura: _____

b. La contaminación del aire: _____

c. Lo que me preocupa: _____

d. La falta de agua: _____

e. Los desechos tóxicos: _____

f. El gran despilfarro: _____

g. Los vehículos contaminantes: _____

h. Reciclamos el papel: _____

i. La contaminación del agua: _____

j. Siempre hace buen tiempo: _____

k. La grave amenaza: _____

l. Yo apago las luces: _____

m. Yo tiro la basura: _____

n. Limpias el cubo de basura: _____

o. Las fábricas contaminan: _____

p. Una bici limpia: _____

9. Translate into English.

a. La contaminación del agua es el principal problema de mi región.

b. Lo que más me preocupa es la contaminación del aire.

c. Siempre hay muchos vehículos contaminantes que circulan por las carreteras.

d. Lo que más me sorprende es ver la cantidad de basura que la gente tira en las calles.

e. Los coches eléctricos son muy caros pero también son buenos para el medioambiente.

f. Creo que es muy importante proteger el medioambiente.

g. Compro la menor cantidad posible de ropa y dono mi ropa vieja a organizaciones benéficas.

h. Siempre uso el transporte público para contaminar menos.

i. Reciclo los plásticos, las latas y el papel.

j. Creo que el cambio climático es el problema más importante en el mundo.

k. En mi opinión, la gente no se preocupa lo suficiente por el medioambiente.

l. Creo que voy a esforzarme más en el futuro.

m. No soy optimista sobre el futuro del planeta.

Foundation reading

1. **Read these comments about what young people do for the environment.**

> **Laura**
> Compro la menor cantidad posible de ropa y dono mis libros viejos a las tiendas que los venden.
>
> **Samuel**
> Siempre uso el transporte público para contaminar menos. También voy en bicicleta muy a menudo.
>
> **Carlos**
> Yo reciclo los plásticos, las latas y el papel. Además, no como ni carne ni pescado.

Who says what? Put a cross in the correct column for each question.

Who...	Laura	Samuel	Carlos
a. ...uses public transport?			
b. ...recycles plastic and paper?			
c. ...buys as few clothes as possible?			
d. ...is vegetarian?			
e. ...gives old books to shops?			
f. ...uses their bicycle very often?			

2. **Read this online message from Damián.**

 Mañana voy a ir al campo con mis amigos. Vamos a plantar árboles para el club ecologista de nuestra escuela. Yo creo que es muy importante esforzarse un poco para proteger el planeta. De hecho, el fin de semana pasado mi madre compró un vehículo eléctrico.

Complete the gap in each sentence using a word from the box below. There are more words than gaps.

> bike   city   car   mountains
> flowers   countryside   trees

a. Damián is going to go into the _____

b. He is going to plant _____

c. Last weekend his mother bought an electric _____

Foundation reading

3. **Read what these people think about electric cars.**

Indiana
Con el coche eléctrico podemos conducir sin contaminar. No veo ningún problema.

Mohamed
Los coches eléctricos son muy caros, por lo que es imposible para la gente sin recursos comprar uno.

Paloma
Los coches eléctricos son demasiado caros. Sin embargo, también es cierto que son buenos para el medioambiente.

Marcos
Me gustaría comprarme un coche eléctrico algún día porque son rápidos y limpios. Son una gran ventaja para el planeta.

If the person has a positive opinion put P in the box. If they have a negative opinion put N in the box. If they express both a positive and negative opinion put P/N in the box.

Indiana ☐   Mohamed ☐   Paloma ☐   Marcos ☐

4. **Three people are giving their opinion about pollution in their region.**

Leonardo

La contaminación del agua es el problema principal en nuestra región. En mi opinión, el agua está muy contaminada.

Sebastián

Lo que más me asusta es la contaminación atmosférica. Siempre hay muchos vehículos contaminantes en las carreteras.

Vega

Odio ver la cantidad de papel y otros tipos de basura que la gente tira en la calle y a lo largo de las carreteras principales. ¡Es horrible!

Circle the correct answer in each case.

1. Leonardo's main issue is with: (a) noise   (b) water   (c) air

2. Sebastián's main issue is with: (a) air   (b) rubbish   (c) plastic

3. Vega's main issue is with: (a) water   (b) noise   (c) litter

Foundation reading

5. **Read Jimena's comment about the environment. Then answer the questions in English.**

Creo que la crisis climática es el problema más importante en el mundo.

No entiendo por qué los gobiernos no hacen lo suficiente para reducir las emisiones de gases.

Estoy de acuerdo con los jóvenes que hacen huelga y se niegan a ir a la escuela. No soy optimista sobre el futuro del planeta.

a. What is Jimena's main concern? _____

b. What does she say about governments? _____

c. What does she agree with? _____

d. How does she feel about the future? _____

6. **Read this article about environmental issues in Nicaragua.**

En Nicaragua, la contaminación del agua es un problema importante ya que muchos ríos de varias regiones están contaminados. Hay que reducir la contaminación de las fábricas y de la actividad minera. Esta fuente de energía no es limpia por lo que hay que utilizar recursos energéticos más sostenibles.

Además, los bosques son cada vez más pequeños debido a la agricultura. Hay que protegerlos.

Complete the table below.

Problem	Solution
Water pollution	

7. **Read this description of an environmental problem in Chile, a Spanish-speaking country in South America. Then answer the questions in English.**

El calentamiento global está teniendo graves consecuencias en Sudamérica. En Chile las temperaturas han aumentado en los últimos años y las olas de calor son cada vez más frecuentes. Además, cada vez llueve menos: en la zona central y sur del país las precipitaciones han bajado un 30% desde los años 80. Estos cambios contribuyen a la existencia de más incendios forestales. Por último, hay menos nieve en los Andes con pérdidas de hasta el 60% de la nieve en algunas áreas y se prevé que los glaciares se derritan y desaparezcan en los próximos años.

a. What is causing problems in Chile? _____

b. What is behind the increase in the number of wild fires? _____

c. What has happened in the country's central area? _____

d. What might happen with the glaciars in the future? _____

Higher vocabulary building

Vocabulary

las afueras	*suburbs*
alrededores	*vicinity*
advertir	*to warn*
apagar	*to turn off*
el árbol	*tree*
el barrio	*neighbourhood*
la bolsa	*bag*
bonito	*pretty*
la caja	*box*
la calefacción	*heating*
el campo	*countryside*
el ciudadano	*citizen*
construir	*to build*
dar	*to give*
destruir	*to destroy*
dirigir	*to direct*
encender	*to turn on*
energía	*energy*
energía eólica	*wind power*
la fábrica	*factory*
fabricar	*to manufacture*
el hambre	*hunger*
la guerra	*war*
el habitante	*inhabitant*
el impuesto	*tax*
preocupación	*concern*
limpio	*clean*
la lluvia	*rain*
luchar	*to fight*
el lugar	*place*
la madera	*wood*
la muerte	*death*
malgastar	*to waste*
necesario	*necessary*
el paisaje	*landscape/scenery*
la pobreza	*poverty*
proteger	*to protect*
quemar	*to burn*
reciclar	*to recycle*
renovable	*renewable*
el río	*river*
la riqueza	*wealth*
salvar	*to save, to rescue*
seguro	*safe, sure*
sucio	*dirty*
sufrir	*to suffer*
el sufrimiento	*suffering*
el vidrio	*glass*
el viento	*wind*

1. Match up.

Amenaza	Glass
Encender	War
Afueras	Wood
Guerra	Threat
Madera	Dirty
Vidrio	To turn on
Sucio	Hunger
Hambre	Suburbs
Necesidad	Clean
Limpio	Safe
Seguro	Need

2. Correct the wrong translations.

a. Gestionar: To manage _____

b. Caja: Wood _____

c. Hambre: Hunger _____

d. Intenso: Smelly _____

e. Quemar: To turn on _____

f. Lugar: Tax _____

g. Preocupado: Sad _____

h. Dar: To take _____

3. One of three – circle the right answers.

Amenaza	tax	threat	place
Dar	to give	to pay	to destroy
Paisaje	village	tax	scenery
Luchar	to turn	to fight	to stay
Impuesto	tax	rubbish	impostor
Sucio	pretty	dirty	clean
Seguro	safe	poor	Dirty
Vidrio	wood	glass	Paper
Limpio	nice	clean	Limpet
Guerra	war	wood	metal
Fábrica	hunger	usage	factory

4. Tick and translate any adjectives.

a. Preocupado

b. Caja

c. Guapo

d. Sucio

e. Limpio

f. Afueras

g. Muerte

h. Lluvia

i. Seguro

j. Solar

5. Complete the translations.

a. La contaminación de los ríos: Pollution of the _____

b. La lluvia ácida: Acid _____

c. Un pueblo limpio: A _____ town

d. Un barrio seguro: A _____ neighbourhood

e. Aumentar los impuestos: To increase _____

f. El sufrimiento de los animales: The _____ of animals

6. Translate into English.

a. Limpio _____

b. Guardar _____

c. Luchar _____

d. Amenaza _____

e. Impuesto _____

f. Preocupado _____

g. Paisaje _____

h. Destruir _____

i. Sucio _____

j. Solar _____

k. Fábrica _____

l. Guerra _____

7. Sentence puzzle (put the words in each sentence in the right order).

a. plástico Debemos usar de bolsas evitar   [We must avoid using plastic bags]
_____

b. Hay que emisiones de gas reducir carbono las   [We must reduce carbon gas emissions]
_____

c. de limitar el Es consumo necesario agua   [It is necessary to limit water consumption]
_____

d. peligro las de extinción Debemos especies en salvar   [We must save endangered species]
_____

e. basura importante Es reciclar la   [It is important to recycle waste]
_____

f. vivir y Quiero en un limpio barrio seguro   [I want to live in a clean and safe neighbourhood]
_____

g. mi paisaje bonito alrededor de pueblo El es muy   [The landscape around my town is very beautiful]
_____

8. Translate into English.

a. Las bolsas de plástico.   _____   i. Plantar árboles.   _____

b. Hay que reciclar.   _____   j. Encender las luces.   _____

c. Un barrio sucio.   _____   k. Reciclar la madera.   _____

d. La contaminación de los ríos. _____   l. La necesidad de energía.   _____

e. Lo peor es el ruido.   _____   m. Un paisaje bonito.   _____

f. Los vehículos contaminantes. _____   n. Es preocupante.   _____

g. Aumentar los impuestos.   _____   o. La vida en el campo.   _____

h. La amenaza de extinción.   _____   p. Las fábricas contaminan.   _____

9. Translate into English.

a. Las turbinas eólicas son limpias y más baratas.   _____

b. Acabo de leer un artículo sobre la crisis climática.   _____

c. El nivel del mar subirá en el futuro.   _____

d. Las energías renovables serán indispensables.   _____

e. Tendremos que luchar para proteger el medio ambiente.   _____

f. Las personas sin recursos son quienes más sufren.   _____

g. Las especies raras están en peligro de extinción.   _____

h. En mi opinión, este es el tema más importante.   _____

i. La energía nuclear tendrá un papel importante.   _____

j. He decidido comprar menos ropa nueva.   _____

k. Mi madre no viajará más en avión.   _____

l. El cambio climático me preocupa.   _____

m. Los gobiernos tendrán que hacer más.   _____

Higher reading

1. **Read about an environmental project Marcos took part in. Then answer the questions in English.**

La semana pasada participé en un muy buen proyecto medioambiental. Mis amigos y yo limpiamos nuestro barrio recogiendo basura y plantando árboles. Fue una experiencia fantástica porque aprendimos la importancia de trabajar juntos y de cuidar nuestro planeta.

Tomamos conciencia de la importancia de adoptar hábitos respetuosos con el medio ambiente. Gracias a este proyecto, hemos contribuido a que nuestra comunidad esté más limpia y sea más verde. También nos ha permitido establecer relaciones más sólidas con nuestros vecinos y formar parte de un cambio positivo. Participar en acciones respetuosas con el medio ambiente no sólo es bueno para la naturaleza, sino también para nosotros mismos y para las generaciones futuras.

a. What type of things did Marcos and his friends do? Mention two details.

_____

b. What did they learn from the project? Mention two details.

_____

c. How did taking part in the project affect relationships with neighbours?

_____

d. What does Marcos say in the final sentence? Mention two details.

_____

2. **Read this comment Lisa made about environmental issues.**

No es la contaminación local lo que me preocupa. En mi opinión, lo más importante es el cambio climático global. La semana pasada participé en una huelga para protestar contra la construcción de un nuevo aeropuerto en mi región. Pronto escribiré un artículo sobre el medioambiente para la revista de mi colegio.

Tick which two of the following statements are correct?

a. Lisa is most worried about pollution in her local area. ☐

b. She recently took part in a protest. ☐

c. A new airport is planned for her region. ☐

d. She has written an article for her school magazine. ☐

Higher reading

3. **Read about Abel's involvement in environmental issues.**

Abel siempre se ha mostrado comprometido con el medioambiente: de pequeño, participó en un proyecto local en el que recogía residuos para proteger el ecosistema local y desde hace dos años trabaja para una asociación que recicla objetos y los entrega a desempleados.

Dentro de unos días participará en un proyecto para crear un nuevo jardín en una escuela primaria. Pronto Abel ayudará a poner en marcha una iniciativa en la escuela para animar a la gente a utilizar menos plástico.

What does the article say about these events? In each box, write P for something that happened in the past, N for something that is happening now, F for something that will happen in the future.

a. A local clean-up campaign. ☐

c. Creating a garden in a school. ☐

b. Recycling goods for the unemployed. ☐

d. A project to reduce plastic use. ☐

4. **Read this article about environmental issues in Canarias, a set of Spanish islands located off the coast of northwestern Africa.**

La belleza natural de estas islas está amenazada por varios problemas. El aumento del nivel del mar debido al cambio climático es una amenaza constante. También se están destruyendo paisajes de alto nivel ecológico por ser el hogar de muchas especies de animales y plantas.

Además, el número de turistas está provocando un consumo excesivo de los recursos locales. Los habitantes de Canarias son conscientes de estos problemas y buscan soluciones para proteger sus islas. Hay proyectos en marcha para preservar el litoral, fomentar el turismo ecorresponsable y proteger las especies animales. Todo ello para asegurar el frágil equilibrio de estas islas del Atlántico. Es muy importante que trabajemos juntos para preservar la vida natural de las Canarias.

In English, write relevant information from the article.

a. Threats to the environment of Canary Islands. Mention three points.

_____

b. The response of local inhabitants.

_____

c. Initiatives which respond to the environmental problems. Mention three points.

_____

d. Overall aim of initiatives.

_____

Higher reading

5. Read about these apps which help people reduce their carbon footprint.

Breezo Meter

Descarga esta aplicación para conocer la calidad del aire en una ubicación específica. Utiliza esta app sobre todo si tienes problemas de salud como asma.

GoGreen Challenge

¿Te cuesta seguir un estilo de vida responsable con el medioambiente? La aplicación "GoGreen Challenge" te propone retos diarios y semanales para ser más verdes.

Too Good To Go

"Too Good To Go" encuentra restaurantes y pequeñas tiendas que ofrecen la comida no vendida a precios reducidos.

Greenly

Para conocer el impacto medioambiental de lo que compras, "Greenly" es una aplicación conectada a la de tu banco, que te ofrece precios reducidos si usas marcas ecológicas.

Blablacar

Para reducir tu impacto ecológico, comparte tus trayectos en coche con otras personas. La aplicación "Blablacar" te pone en contacto con conductores que tienen plazas libres.

Name the app...

    a. ...which links to your bank account, offering lower prices.   _____

    b. ...where drivers offer spare seats in their vehicle for journeys.   _____

    c. ...which provides information about air pollution levels   _____

    d. ...which helps reduce food waste.   _____

    e. ...which suggests daily challenges to help protect the environment.   _____

6. Read this information about a company called Greenweez. Then answer the questions in English.

En 2009, Javier Goyeneche decidió crear ropa a partir de materiales reciclados a través de la marca Ecoalf. Además, un año más tarde creó una fundación con el mismo nombre para la limpieza de los mares. Javier creó estos proyectos después de fundar una marca de bolsos y accesorios y ver la cantidad de desechos que produce la industria de la moda.

Varios años más tarde, la empresa tiene presencia en más de 1.800 tiendas multimarca en 40 países. También tiene tiendas propias en cinco países: cuatro en Europa y una en Asia. Por último, Ecoalf emplea a 150 trabajadores.

---

    a. What does Ecoalf do? Mention two points.

    _____

    b. How did it start out?   _____

    c. Two figures about the company.   _____

Grammar focus   The Conditional Tense

Below are some examples of the Conditional in use with translations on the right.

Yo **reciclaría** la basura más a menudo.	I **would recycle** waste more often.
Compraría más productos de segunda mano.	I **would buy** more second-hand products.
Haría un esfuerzo mayor.	I **would make** a greater effort.
Me gustaría proteger el medioambiente.	I **would like** to protect the environment.

So, the conditional usually translates as "would do" something. It refers to something you might do in the future but hasn't happened yet.

But it doesn't always translate as "would." Look at these examples:

Yo **podría** reciclar más cosas.	I **might/could** recycle more things.
Debería tomar el avión menos a menudo.	I **should/ought to** take the plane less often.

In the GCSE exam, if you show you can use the Conditional, you can gain extra marks for complexity of language, so use it if you can.

Noticing the conditional

After each sentence below mark it with PRES, FUT or COND to show you recognise the difference between present, future, and conditional. Translate each sentence to show you know exactly what it means.

Ejemplo: Yo comería menos carne.	COND	I would eat less meat.
a. Yo reciclaré más papel.		
b. Él reciclará más plásticos.		
c. Siempre apago las luces.		
d. Yo utilizaría el transporte público.		
e. Tú viajarás en avión menos a menudo.		
f. Mi familia recicla un montón de basura.		
g. Nosotros viajaremos en coche eléctrico.		
h. Nosotros viajaríamos en un coche híbrido.		
i. Nosotros viajamos a menudo en tren.		
j. Yo podría reducir mi huella de carbono.		
k. Yo debería comer menos carne.		
l. Yo podría comer productos orgánicos.		
m. Me gustaría consumir menos energía.		
n. Nosotros reciclamos papel y vidrio.		
o. Yo uso mi bici a menudo.		
p. Yo compraré productos orgánicos.		
q. Yo compraría menos ropa nueva.		

The Conditional Tense

Regular verbs		
Cambiar - *to change*	**Encender** - *to turh on*	**Reducir** - *to reduce*
Yo cambiar**ía**	Yo encender**ía**	Yo reducir**ía**
Tú cambiar**ías**	Tú encender**ías**	Tú reducir**ías**
Él/ella/usted cambiar**ía**	Él/ella/usted encender**ía**	Él/ella/usted reducir**ía**
Nosotros cambiar**íamos**	Nosotros encender**íamos**	Nosotros reducir**íamos**
Vosotros cambiar**íais**	Vosotros encender**íais**	Vosotros reducir**íais**
Ellos/ustedes cambiar**ían**	Ellos/ustedes encender**ían**	Ellos/ustedes reducir**ían**

Irregular verbs (verbs with irregular stems)			
Hacer *to do*	Yo har**ía** ... *I would do*	**Decir** *to say*	Yo dir**ía** ... *I would say*
Poder *to be able to*	Yo podr**ía** ... *I would be able to*	**Saber** *to know*	Yo sabr**ía** ... *I would know*
Salir *to go out*	Yo saldr**ía** ... *I would go out*	**Tener** *to have*	Yo tendr**ía** ... *I would have*

1. Match up.

Destruir	To clean
Tirar	To pollute
Actuar	To destroy
Limpiar	To improve
Contaminar	To throw away
Mejorar	To travel
Viajar	To act
Utilizar	To increase
Aumentar	To reduce
Reducir	To use

2. Complete the table.

Infinitive	Future	Conditional Tense
Reciclar	Yo reciclaré	Yo reciclaría
Vivir	Nosotros viviremos	
Limpiar	Ellos limpiarán	
Comprar	Tú comprarás	
Mejorar	Ellos mejorarán	
Tener	Nosotros tendremos	
Poder	Vosotros podréis	
Querer	Yo querré	
Deber	Ellos deberán	
Vender	Tú venderás	

3. Choose the correct conditional ending.

a. Nosotros reciclar**íamos/íais/ían** más.

b. Las especies raras ya no estar**íamos/íais/ían** en peligro de extinción.

c. Yo comprar**ía/ías/ían** más productos frescos.

d. Vosotros construir**íamos/íais/ían** menos edificios.

e. Habr**ía/ías/ían** más cubos de basura.

f. Ellos usar**íamos/íais/ían** menos el coche.

g. Vosotros no tirar**íamos/íais/ían** la basura al suelo.

h. Yo viajar**ía/ías/ían** menos en avión.

i. Tú te esforzar**ía/ías/ían** más.

j. Yo deber**ía/ías/ían** esforzarme más.

k. Nosotros plantar**íamos/íais/ían** más árboles.

4. Complete with the correct conditional ending.

a. Yo reciclar _ _ más.

b. Ellos cambiar_ _ _ sus costumbres.

c. Nosotros esperar_ _ _ _ _ un cambio.

d. Vosotros actuar_ _ _ _ para mejorar las cosas.

e. Ellos destruir_ _ _ más bosques.

f. Yo reducir_ _ mi consumo.

g. Nosotros deber _ _ _ _ _ eliminar el plástico.

h. Habr_ _ que reutilizar las bolsas.

i. Yo querr _ _ plantar árboles.

j. El gobierno podr_ _ hacer más.

k. Las fábricas contaminar _ _ _ más.

5. Anagrams: rewrite the verbs correctly.

e.g. Ellos *acreiclarín* (they would recycle) *ellos reciclarían*

a. Nosotros *acerrímoidus* (we would reduce) _____

b. Ella *ambicíara* (she would change) _____

c. Ellos *ansíoncurtir* (they would build) _____

d. Yo *acuítara* (I would act) _____

e. Ellos *envídaren* (they would sell) _____

f. Vosotros *ahíiras* (you would do) _____

g. Yo *raívivi* (I would live) _____

6. Correct the endings of the Spanish verbs below.

a. Yo harías   (I would do)

b. Ellos esperaríamos (they would wait)

c. Vosotros irías   (you would go)

d. Él querríais   (he would want)

e. Nosotros serían   (we would be)

f. Yo podríais   (I could)

g. Nosotros viviría   (we would live)

7. Translate into Spanish.

a. I would recycle   _____

b. I would change   _____

c. I would do   _____

d. I should be   _____

e. I could live   _____

f. I would increase   _____

g. I would stop   _____

h. I would buy   _____

i. You (sing). would recycle   _____

j. We should consume   _____

k. They (M) could buy   _____

l. She would like to do _____

m. You (pl). could use   _____

n. They (F) would destroy _____

o. We could travel   _____

p. They (M) should reduce _____

8. ¿Qué harías… (what would you do…) – use the verbs below to help you complete the sentences

a. …si hubiera pocos árboles en tu ciudad? _____ más árboles

b. …si viajaras en avión a menudo? _____ en tren o en barco

c. …si fueras al trabajo cada día con el coche? _____ andando o en bicicleta

d. …si el gobierno no hiciera nada? _____ una manifestación

e. …si no quisieras un coche tradicional? _____ un coche de hidrógeno

| compraría | viajaría | iría | organizaría | plantaría |

9. Translate into Spanish.

a. I would like to buy fewer clothes. _____

b. I should try to use the car less often. _____

c. I would change my habits in the future. _____

d. We would recycle paper, plastic and glass. _____

e. There would be (careful!) less pollution. _____

f. The future would be cleaner and better. _____

g. I would waste less energy at home. _____

h. We would travel by public transport. _____

i. People would be happier and healthier. _____

Preparing for speaking and writing

1. Complete with the missing letters (there are two missing in each sentence).

z	l	f	t	v	e	j	ñ	u	i	l	b	o	d	y	p

a. Yo r_cic_o un poco pero no lo suficiente. [I do some recycling but not enough]

b. Yo utili_o el transporte público tan_o como puedo. [I use public transport as much as I can]

c. Las _ábricas contam_nan. [Factories pollute the air]

d. _o que me preoc_pa es el calentamiento global. [What worries me is climate warming]

e. Yo _ivo en un peque_o pueblo en el sur. [I live in a small town in the south]

f. El paisa_e alrede_or de mi pueblo es bonito. [The landscape around my town is beautiful]

g. Mi _arrio es muy lim_io y seguro. [My neighbourhood is very clean and safe]

h. Ellos constru_en demasiados edificios y aut_pistas. [They build too many buildings and motorways]

2. Anagrams.

a. calcejire:_____ [recycling]

b. guaa: _____ [water]

c. urdio: _____ [noise]

d. blsoas: _____ [bags]

e. dirustre: _____ [to destroy]

f. diviro: _____ [glass]

g. ajaspie: _____ [landscape]

h. álberos: _____ [trees]

3. Complete with the missing verbs.

a. Yo _____ el papel. [I recycle paper]

b. Yo _____ en bicicleta. [I cycle]

c. Yo _____ vegetariana. [I am vegetarian]

d. Yo no _____ la electricidad. [I don't waste electricity]

e. Yo _____ en una ciudad. [I live in a city]

f. _____ un montón de ruido. [There is a lot of noise]

g. Debemos _____ las emisiones. [We must reduce emissions]

4. Match up.

Basura	Factory
Mar	Threat
Vidrio	Sea
Fábrica	Waste
Amenaza	Building
Calentamiento	Renewable
Edificio	Glass
Renovable	Tree
Lugar	To destroy
Destruir	Earth
Tierra	Warming
Árbol	Place

5. Split sentences.

El mar está muy (1)	el calentamiento global.
Hay que reciclar	contaminado en mi región. (1)
En mi pueblo no hay	el paisaje.
Las fábricas	los plásticos.
Mi ciudad es	público.
Lo que me preocupa es	mucho que hacer.
Ellos destruyen	va a tener un papel importante.
La gente malgasta	pequeña y bonita.
Yo utilizo el transporte	los recursos naturales.
La energía solar	contaminan mucho.

6. Complete the translations.

a. The recycling of waste: El r_____ de la _____.

b. The destruction of forests: La d_____ de los _____.

c. The waste of natural resources: El m_____ de r_____ naturales.

d. Greenhouse gases: Los g_____ de efecto i_____.

e. Too many buildings: D_____ e_____.

f. Around my town: A_____ de mi p_____.

g. A dirty and polluted neighbourhood: Un b_____ sucio y c_____.

h. The pollution of the sea: La c_____ del m_____.

---

7. Put the verbs in the infinitive in the *Yo* and *Nosotros* version as shown in the example.

Encender	(to turn on)	*Yo enciendo*	*Nosotros encendemos*
Aumentar	**(to increase)**		
Conducir	**(to drive)**		
Consumir	**(to consume)**		
Malgastar	**(to waste)**		
Tirar	**(to throw)**		
Contaminar	**(to pollute)**		
Reciclar	**(to recycle)**		
Salvar	**(to save)**		

---

8. Translation (easier).

a. I live in a small town in England.

b. My town is pretty and clean.

c. The landscape near my town is beautiful.

d. There are many trees and flowers.

e. My family recycles paper, glass and plastics.

f. We never use plastic bags.

g. The climate crisis is dangerous for the planet.

h. The temperature increases every year.

i. I'm not going to travel by plane next year.

j. I always use public transport.

k. I don't throw rubbish on the ground.

l. On Saturday I recycled some bottles.

m. I'm going to plant a tree.

n. Last weekend I took the bus.

---

9. Translation (harder).

a. What worries me the most is global warming.

b. Water pollution is a big problem in my region.

c. My city is very noisy, dirty and polluted.

d. The government should do more.

e. They build too many buildings and motorways.

f. The worst thing is the destruction of forests.

g. People do not recycle their waste enough.

h. We should recycle more and consume less water and electricity.

i. In my family we recycle waste and avoid using too much water.

j. We also never use the car for short trips.

k. Solar energy should play a more important role.

l. If it were possible, I would travel less often by plane.

m. I shall try not to travel by plane.

Writing and speaking from a photo card

Write something about both of these photos. Write about who you see, where they are what they are doing. Read out your description.

_____   _____

_____   _____

_____   _____

Answer the following questions related to this topic. Read out your answers.

1. En tu opinión, ¿cuáles crees que son los problemas medioambientales más importantes?

   _____

   _____

2. ¿Qué haces para proteger el medio ambiente?

   _____

   _____

3. Habla de la ciudad o pueblo donde vives.

   _____

   _____

4. ¿Qué has hecho recientemente en tu ciudad?

   _____

   _____

5. ¿Qué vas a hacer el fin de semana que viene?

   _____

Speaking in a role-play

Look at the instructions on the left as they would appear in a speaking test. Read aloud with a partner the dialogue on the right. Then do the dialogue a second time, changing the answers in bold. Take turns playing the two roles.

Foundation (Where you see …, your partner makes up a short answer as if they were an examiner).

1. Mention one thing you do to protect the environment.	1. ¿Qué haces para proteger el medioambiente ? **Yo soy vegetariana.**
2. Give one reason why you should protect the environment.	2. ¿Por qué es importante proteger el medioambiente ? **Porque el cambio climático amenaza el planeta.**
3. Ask your friend a question about the environment.	3. ¿Qué crees que tiene que hacer el gobierno por el medioambiente? …
4. Describe your town/village (give one detail).	4. Háblame de tu pueblo o ciudad. **Mi ciudad es histórica, pequeña y muy segura.**
5. Say what you do in your town/village (give one detail).	5. ¿Qué haces en tu pueblo o ciudad? **Voy de compras y juego al rugby.**

Higher (Where you see …, your partner makes up a short answer as if they were an examiner).

1. Describe an environmental problem (give two details).	1. En tu opinión, ¿qué problemas medioambientales son más importantes? **La crisis climática y la contaminación del agua.**
2. Describe something you do to protect the environment (give one opinion and one reason).	2. ¿Qué haces para proteger el medioambiente y por qué? **Yo reciclo la basura porque no hay que desperdiciar los recursos.**
3. Ask your friend a question about the environment.	3. ¿Qué medidas promueve el gobierno de tu ciudad para proteger el medioambiente? …
4. Give one advantage and one disadvantage of electric cars.	4. ¿Qué opinas sobre los coches eléctricos? **Son limpios pero caros.**
5. Say something about nuclear power (give one detail).	5. ¿Qué piensas sobre la energía nuclear? **Creo que es peligrosa.**

Foundation writing

Describe the photo. Write four short sentences in Spanish.

1. _____

2. _____

3. _____

4. _____

Foundation/Higher writing

Write to your friend about the environment. You must include the following points:
• A major problem for the planet
• Your opinion of this issue with a reason
• What you have done recently to help the planet
• Something you will do in the future.
Write about 90 words.

_____

_____

_____

_____

_____

_____

_____

_____

_____

Higher writing

1. **Write about the environment for an online magazine. You must include the following points:** • What concerns you the most • An issue in your local area or region • What you or your family have done to limit your carbon footprint • What you intend to do in the future.
   Write your answer in Spanish. You should aim to write between 130 and 150 words.

2. **Translate the paragraph below.**
   I like buying green products at the supermarket. We recycle lots of things each week. I don't travel by plane. Last week my friends and I went to Paris by train. I want to continue to protect the planet in the future. The environment is an important subject for me.

Foundation sentence bank

Yo creo que el clima es un tema importante.	I think that climate is an important subject.
La crisis climática es peligrosa para el planeta.	The climate crisis is dangerous for the planet.
La temperatura aumenta cada año.	The temperature is increasing s every year.
Hay mucha contaminación en mi ciudad.	There is a lot of pollution in my city.
Yo no tiro basura al suelo.	I don't throw litter on the ground.
Nosotros reciclamos el papel y el plástico.	We recycle paper and plastic.
Nuestro barrio es muy limpio.	Our neighborhood is very clean.
Yo voy a comprar menos ropa.	I am going to buy fewer clothes.
Intento no contaminar el medioambiente.	I try not to pollute the environment.
Yo no voy a viajar en avión el año que viene.	I'm not going to travel by plane next year.
Yo soy vegetariana para proteger el planeta.	I am vegetarian to protect the planet.
Reducimos la cantidad de basura que producimos.	We reduce the amount of waste we produce.
Los ríos están muy contaminados en mi región.	The rivers are polluted in my region.
El domingo pasado reciclé basura.	Last Sunday I recycled some waste.

....

Higher sentence bank

Proteges el planeta reduciendo tu huella de carbono	You protect the planet by reducing your footprint.
Acabo de leer un artículo sobre la crisis climática.	I've just read an article about the climate crisis.
En el futuro los niveles del océano aumentarán.	In the future ocean levels will rise.
Las energías renovables serán cruciales.	Renewable energy will be crucial.
Tendremos que luchar para proteger el medioambiente.	We'll have to fight to protect the environment.
Las poblaciones pobres son las que más sufren.	Poor populations suffer the most.
Las especies raras están en peligro de extinción debido a la crisis climática.	Rare species are in danger of extinction because of the climate crisis.
En mi opinión, es el tema más importante.	In my opinion, it's the most important subject.
La energía nuclear tendría un papel muy importante.	Nuclear energy would play a very important role.
Te aconsejo utilizar el transporte público.	I advise you to use public transport.
Decidí comprar menos ropa nueva.	I decided to buy fewer new clothes.
Mi padre ya no viaja en avión, lo cual me gusta.	My father no longer travels by plane, which I like.
Me gustaría hacer más por el medioambiente.	I would like to do more for the environment.
Los gobiernos deberían esforzarse más.	Governments should make more effort.

UNIT 4

Customs, festivals and celebrations

Contents

- Foundation vocab building.
- Foundation reading.
- Higher vocab building.
- Higher reading.
- Grammar focus – the Perfect Tense.
- Preparing for speaking and writing.
- Writing and speaking from a photo card.
- Speaking in a role play.
- Writing.
- Sentence bank.

Foundation vocab building

Vocabulary

la alegría	happiness
animado	lively
el Año Nuevo	New Year
bailar	to dance
el budista	Buddhist
cantar	to sing
casarse	to get married
católico	Catholic
celebrar	celebrate
la comida	meal
compartir	to share
comprar	to buy
creer	to believe
cristiano	Christian
dar	to give
descubrir	to discover
el desfile	parade, procession
el día festivo	public holiday
el dios/Dios	god/God
disfrutar	to enjoy
Eïd	Eïd
enviar	to send
el evento	event
la fe	faith
feliz	happy
la fiesta	festival, party
felicitar	to congratulate
los fuegos artificiales	fireworks
la iglesia	church
judío	Jewish
loco	mad, crazy
el mundo	world
musulmán	Muslim
la Navidad	Christmas
la Pascua	Easter
quemar	to burn
recibir	to receive
el regalo	gift
religioso	religious
el rey	king
rezar	to pray
la Semana Santa	Easter Week
San Valentín	Valentine's Day
el vino	wine

1. Match up.

Celebrar	To give, offer
Rezar	To get married
Bailar	To receive
Ofrecer	To share
Enviar	To celebrate
Recibir	To wish
Compartir	To dance
Felicitar	To pray
Desear	To congratulate
Casarse	To send

2. Complete with the missing letters.

a. Dio_ (God)

b. Re_alo (gift)

c. Ce_ebrar (to celebrate)

d. Feli_ (happy)

e. Ju_ío (Jewish)

f. Co_ida (meal)

g. O_recer (to give, offer)

h. F_esta (festival, party)

i. El de_f_le (the parade)

3. Complete.

a. Vamos a la iglesia el domingo: We go to _____ on Sunday.

b. Celebramos el Año Nuevo: We celebrate _____ .

c. Yo creo en Dios: I believe in _____.

d. Recibimos regalos: We receive _____.

e. Ellos me dieron dinero: They give me _____.

f. Nosotros cantamos y bailamos: We _____ and dance.

g. Los musulmanes ayunan: _____ fast.

h. Es mi fiesta favorita: It is my favourite _____.

4. Put the phrases below in the correct order.

a. fiesta religiosa una [A religious festival]

b. comida la Navidad de [The Christmas meal]

c. San Valentín de Día el [Saint Valentine's Day]

d. misa la Pascua de [Easter mass]

e. de el Ramadán ayuno [Ramadan fasting]

f. artificiales los fuegos [Fireworks]

g. regalos Navidad los de [Christmas gifts]

h. budista templo un [A Buddhist temple]

i. favorita mi fiesta [My favourite festival]

j. mi con familia toda [With all my family]

k. en mis padres casa de [At my parents' house]

l. los Magos Reyes [The Three Wise Men]

5. Spot and correct the wrong translations.

a. Es mi fiesta favorita: It is my favourite day.

b. Yo veo a mis amigos: I see my family.

c. Celebramos los Reyes Magos: We celebrate Easter.

d. Los cristianos van a la iglesia: My friends go to church.

e. Ellos se casan hoy: They celebrate today.

f. Los judíos celebran Yom Kippur: Jews like Yom Kippur.

g. Me encantan los fuegos artificiales: I love Christmas.

h. Yo recibo un montón de regalos: I receive a lot of money.

i. Las familias se reúnen: Families celebrate.

j. Lo pasamos bien: We have a bad time.

6. Tick all religious words.

a. Iglesia   k. Musulmán

b. Cristiano   l. Budista

c. Judío   m. Fiesta

d. Gente   n. Fuegos artificiales

e. Regalo   o. Dinero

f. Misa   p. Templo

g. Tiempo   q. Mezquita

h. Sol   r. Dios

i. Año Nuevo   s. Festival

j. Catedral   t. Pingüino

7. Wordsearch: find the Spanish translation of the words below.

S	T	M	U	S	U	L	M	A	N	E	S	M	R	N	P	Z	F	N	I
F	A	Ñ	O	N	U	E	V	O	R	C	N	E	E	M	A	X	I	A	G
G	P	E	C	O	M	P	A	R	T	I	R	S	D	Z	R	B	E	V	L
F	U	E	G	O	S	A	R	T	I	F	I	C	I	A	L	E	S	I	E
K	W	P	R	O	C	H	E	S	P	Ê	C	T	O	B	A	F	T	D	S
L	D	G	H	U	P	S	K	L	D	T	P	A	S	C	U	A	A	A	I
C	R	I	S	T	I	A	N	O	S	E	P	A	Q	U	E	S	N	D	A
R	O	E	F	S	F	A	M	I	L	I	A	R	E	S	R	E	Z	A	R

Muslims: m_ _ _ _ _ _ _ _   *fireworks:* f_ _ _ _ _ a_ _ _ _ _ _ _ _ _ _   *Christmas:* N_ _ _ _ _ _

church: i_ _ _ _ _ _   *to pray:* r_ _ _ _   *God:* D_ _ _

to share: c_ _ _ _ _ _ _ _   *festival:* f_ _ _ _ _   *Easter:* P_ _ _ _ _

Christians: c_ _ _ _ _ _ _ _ _   *relatives:* f_ _ _ _ _ _ _ _   *New Year:* A_ _ N _ _ _ _

8. Complete with the options provided.

a. Los _____ artificiales.

b. La _____ va a la iglesia.

c. Prepara la _____ de Navidad.

d. Yo recibo _____.

e. La gente celebra la _____.

f. Nosotros _____.

g. Yo _____ en Dios.

h. Eid es mi fiesta _____.

i. Yo _____ mi cumpleaños con mi familia.

1. fuegos
2. favorita
3. regalos
4. gente
5. creo
6. cantamos
7. comida
8. celebro
9. Navidad

9. Translate into English.

a. Usted va a la iglesia el domingo.

b. Hay fuegos artificiales por Año Nuevo.

c. Nosotros celebramos el Día de la Madre.

d. Los judíos van a la sinagoga.

e. Mucha gente se casa en verano.

f. En muchos pueblos hay fiestas locales.

g. Hay conciertos y desfiles.

h. Los familiares se reúnen para celebrar la fiesta.

i. Yo celebro mi cumpleaños con mis amigos.

Foundation reading

1. **Read these comments about celebrations.**

> **Sandra**
> Mi fiesta favorita es la Navidad, pero también me gusta celebrar los cumpleaños de mis amigos.
>
> **Pablo**
> Para mí, las fiestas musulmanas son importantes. También celebro el Año Nuevo porque es una tradición importante.
>
> **Eva**
> No soy religiosa así que no me interesan esas fiestas pero sí me gusta la Semana Santa, por ejemplo.

Who says what? Put a cross in the correct column for each question.

Who...	Sandra	Pablo	Eva
a. ...is not religious?			
b. ...celebrates friends' birthdays?			
c. ...likes to celebrate Easter?			
d. ...celebrates the New Year?			
e. ...prefers Christmas?			
f. ...values Muslim festivals?			

2. **Three people are describing how they will spend their next birthday, then answer the questions.**

> **Daniela**
> Creo que voy a ir con mis amigos a la playa, no muy lejos de donde vivo. ¡Va a ser estupendo!
>
> **Martina**
> Mi familia y yo vamos a celebrar mi cumpleaños la semana que viene. Vamos a tener una buena comida en la ciudad.
>
> **Antonio**
> Creo que vamos a celebrar mi cumpleaños yendo a ver a mi cantante favorito al teatro de la ciudad.
>
> **Andrés**
> Voy a celebrar mi cumpleaños en casa de una amiga que conozco desde hace 10 años. Será divertido.

    a.   Who will go out to eat?   _____

    b.   Who will go to a beach?   _____

    c.   Who will go to an old friend's house?   _____

    d.   Who will go to a concert?   _____

Foundation reading

3. Read this article about Sonia's visit to a festival in Barichara, Colombia, then answer the questions in English.

El septiembre pasado, fui con mis amigas a un festival de cine medioambiental en Barichara, Colombia. Se celebra una vez al año y es uno de los festivales medioambientales más importantes de Latinoamérica. Yo vi varios documentales magníficos y aprendí mucho sobre la situación del medioambiente en Colombia. Además participé en una actividad de siembra de árboles. Como recuerdo, compré una artesanía de un productor local.

a. When did Sonia go to the festival? _____

b. How often does the festival take place? _____

c. What did she learn about? _____

d. In what activity did she participate? _____

e. What souvenir did she buy? _____

4. Read about these popular festivals in Belgium, then answer the questions in English.

Tapati Rapa Nui
Es un festival que celebra la cultura del pueblo indígena chileno. Se celebra en febrero.

Santiago a Mil
Este festival tiene lugar en enero y gira en torno al teatro. Se presentan obras de teatro nacionales e internacionales en varios puntos de la capital, Santiago de Chile.

Festival de Viña del Mar
Este festival, que se celebra entre febrero y marzo, es uno de los festivales de música más relevantes de Latinoamérica. En él participan importantes cantantes chilenos y del extranjero.

Chile Wine Fest
En este festival, que se celebra en noviembre, los visitantes pueden aprender sobre el vino chileno y disfrutar de degustaciones.

Festival Aéreo Villarrica
En este festival, que sucede al sur del país, se muestran diferentes tipos de aviones y se hacen exhibiciones aéreas.

a. What is Tapati Rapa Nui? _____

b. When does "Santiago a Mil" take place? _____

c. How participates in the "Festival de Viña del Mar"? _____

d. When is the Chile wine festival? _____

e. What type of event takes place in Villarrica? _____

f. Where in the country is Villarrica located? _____

Foundation reading

5. **Read what these young people think about customs and festivals in their region.**

Adam
Creo que las fiestas y festivales de mi región son para adultos, no para adolescentes, así que no me interesan mucho.

Estefanía
Creo que aquí hay una gran variedad de festivales en verano. Pero también creo que hay demasiados turistas.

Martín
Me gusta ir a festivales cerca de donde vivo. Creo que todos son diferentes e interesantes.

Camila
Me encanta el festival de música de Viña del Mar. Lo que no me gusta es el precio de las entradas…

Benjamín
Fui al Festival de las Ciencias en octubre. Me gustaron mucho los talleres* sobre astronomía.

* taller = workshop

What do the people think about the festivals? Write P for a positive opinion, N for a negative opinion, P + N for a positive and negative opinion. Write the correct letter in each box.

Adam ☐   Estefanía ☐   Martín ☐   Camila ☐   Benjamín ☐

6. **Read this text about a celebration in Chile.**

El 21 de junio es un día festivo en Chile porque cada año se celebra en esa fecha el Día Nacional de los Pueblos Indígenas, coincidiendo con el solsticio de invierno. En este festivo se reconoce la importancia de los pueblos indígenas de Chile, como los mapuche o los aymara, y se celebra su cultura.

Todos los años adultos y niños se reúnen en torno a comida tradicional y cuentan historias típicas de las culturas indígenas. También hacen bailes ceremoniales y juegos tradicionales durante todo el día.

Aunque solo el 21 de junio es festivo, esta celebración se extiende hasta el 24 de junio.

Circle the correct answer in each case.

1.	The celebration takes place	a) every two years	b) in July	c) once a year
2.	It's a celebration for	a) adults	b) adults and children	c) children
3.	You can learn about culture	a) before lunch	b) after lunch	c) all day
4.	The celebration last	a) one day	b) two days	c) four days

Higher vocab building

Vocabulary

animado	*lively*
el Año Nuevo	*New Year*
asistir	*to attend*
la boda	*wedding*
budista	*Buddhist*
casarse	*to get married*
católico	*Catholic*
cantar	*to sing*
celebrar	*to celebrate*
la comida	*meal*
compartir	*to share*
comprar	*to buy*
contento	*merry, happy*
cristiano	*Christian*
creer	*to believe*
cumpleaños	*birthday*
descubrir	*to discover*
el día festivo	*public holiday*
el dios/Dios	*god/God*
el desfile	*parade*
el Día de la Madre	*Mother's Day*
Eid	*Eid*
enviar	*to send*
el evento	*event*
la fe	*faith*
felicitar	*to congratulate*
la fiesta	*party, festival*
la felicidad	*happiness*
los fuegos artificiales	*fireworks*
la iglesia	*church*
judío	*Jewish*
quemar	*to burn*
loco	*crazy*
matrimonio	*marriage*
el mundo	*world*
musulmán	*Muslim*
la Navidad	*Christmas*
la Pascua	*Easter*
el pastel, la tarta	*cake*
el regalo	*gift*
recibir	*to receive*
regalar	*to gift*
religioso	*religious*
reunirse	*to gather*
rezar	*to pray*
el rey	*king*
el Roscón de Reyes	*King's Cake*
Semana Santa	*Easter/Holy Week*
la sinagoga	*the synagogue*
el templo	*temple*
el vino	*wine*

1. Match.

Desfile	Gifts	**Cantar**	To receive
Pascua	New Year	**Ofrecer**	Wedding
Fiesta	People	**Contento**	To believe
Año Nuevo	Church	**Boda**	Faith
Musulmán	Christians	**Rezar**	Happy
Gente	Party	**Comida**	To sing
Iglesia	Public holiday	**Enviar**	Happiness
Cristianos	Parade	**Creer**	To pray
Día festivo	Muslim	**Fe**	Event
Niños	Easter	**Recibir**	To offer
Regalos	Children	**Evento**	Meal
Familiares	Relatives	**Felicidad**	To send

2. Gapped translation.

a. Nosotros celebramos el Año Nuevo: *We _____ _____.*

b. Los cristianos van a a la iglesia: _____ *go to* _____.

c. La gente da regalos: _____ *give* _____.

d. Yo disfruto de las vacaciones: *I _____ the _____.*

e. Yo veo a mis familiares: *I _____ my _____.*

f. Mi familia se reúne en mi casa: *My _____ gathers* ___ ___ _____.

g. Yo creo en Dios: *I _____ in _____.*

3. Spot and correct the wrong English translations.

a. Es el día de Año Nuevo:	It's a public holiday.
b. Yo felicito a mis amigos:	I invite my friends.
c. La gente se reúne:	People celebrate.
d. Algunas personas están locas:	Some people are happy.
e. Comemos una buena comida:	We eat a huge meal.
f. Hay una buena comida:	There is a good festival.
g. Eid es una fiesta musulmana:	Eid is a Jewish festival
h. Yo rezo y canto:	I pray and dance.
i. Compartimos un buen momento:	We have a good holiday.
j. Doy regalos a mis familiares:	I give my mother gifts.
k. Celebramos el Día de la Madre:	We celebrate Easter.
l. Nosotros cantamos y bailamos:	I sing and dance.

4. Sentence puzzle - rearrange the words in the right order.

1. celebro comprando Yo regalos la Navidad   [I celebrate Christmas by buying presents]

_____

2. un música gran Acabamos de estar en un festival de   [We've just been to a big music festival]

_____

3. religioso iglesia iría la Si yo fuera a   [If I were religious, I would go to church]

_____

4. la Pascua no Nosotros celebramos casa en   [We do not celebrate Easter at home]

_____

5. En es mi opinión importante las mantener tradiciones [In my opinion it is important to keep traditions].

_____

6. al Diwali festival Yo ir espero en de octubre   [I hope to go to the Diwali festival in October]

_____

5. Find the word for each definition.

a. Una fiesta musulmana: E_ _

b. Una fiesta cristiana: P_ _ _ _ _

c. Se lo damos a los niños en Navidad: r_ _ _ _ _ _

d. La fiesta del amor: S _ _ _ _ _ _ _ _ _

e. Otro verbo para "festejar": c_ _ _ _ _ _ _

f. Un lugar de culto judío: s_ _ _ _ _ _ _

g. Un lugar de culto cristiano: i_ _ _ _ _ _

h. El 25 de diciembre: N_ _ _ _ _ _

i. Sinónimo de "favorito": p_ _ _ _ _ _ _ _

j. Lo contrario de "ofrecer": r _ _ _ _ _ _

6. Split sentences.

Yo creo	regalos.
Ellos celebran	con Felipe.
Nosotros vamos	familiares.
Yo ofrezco	en Dios.
Ella se casa	un buen momento juntos.
Nosotros	el Año Nuevo en mi casa.
Compartimos	artificiales.
Hay fuegos	a la misa de Pascua.
Veo a mis	nos reunimos en mi casa.

7. Translate into English.

a. Un regalo   _____

b. Dios mío   _____

c. Los fuegos artificiales _____

d. Un día festivo   _____

e. El Roscón de Reyes _____

f. Un día de felicidad _____

g. Compartimos   _____

h. Ellos ofrecen   _____

i. Yo recibo   _____

j. Nos reunimos   _____

8. Translate into English.

a. Los Reyes Magos son en enero.

b. Todos los años los musulmanes celebran Eid.

c. Los amigos se reúnen para compartir un buen momento.

d. Las ocasiones especiales suelen ser días festivos.

e. En la mayoría de las ciudades hay desfiles.

f. En Pascua siempre comemos huevos de chocolate.

g. Me encanta ver los fuegos artificiales de Año Nuevo.

h. Me encanta la Navidad porque es mi fiesta favorita.

i. Yo doy regalos a mis padres.

Higher reading

1. Read this article about a festival in Medellín, Colombia. Then answer the questions in English.

Todos los años desde 1957, tiene lugar en Medellín la Feria de las Flores entre julio y agosto. Este es un evento espectacular en el que se celebra la cultura de la región y su tradición de producción de flores (Colombia es el segundo mayor exportador de flores del mundo).

El evento central de la Fiesta de las Flores es el concurso de silletas. Las silletas son creaciones de flores que los hombres o silleteros llevan a la espalda. Estos silleteros llevan la ropa típica de la zona: pantalones oscuros, camisa blanca, sombrero, un bolso especial llamado 'carriel' y el abrigo de los campesinos, que suele ser un poncho, al que se llama 'ruana' en la zona.

Los silleteros desfilan con sus silletas. Después, se eligen las ganadoras en cinco categorías y una creación ganadora final. En esta fiesta también hay otros tipos de eventos como conciertos o exposiciones de flores.

a.   At what time of year does the festival happen?   _____

b.   What is celebrated?   _____

c.   What do the men wear?   _____

d.   What happens after the parade?   _____

2. Read an account by Darío.

Ayer salí con mis amigos a ver una película al cine. Estuvo muy bien. Hoy estoy descansando con mis padres, jugando a un juego de mesa. El sábado iré al festival de música de Lollapalooza Chile. Tocará mi grupo favorito. Me compraré sus camisetas. Ir al festival es una tradición para nosotros y eso me encanta.

Write P for something that happened in the past N for something that is happening now F for something that will happen in the future. Write the correct letter in each box.

a) relaxing at home ☐   c) watching a film ☐

b) buying a souvenir ☐   d) going to a music festival ☐

3. Read Vega's account of her Christmas holiday, then circle the best options.

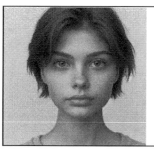

Las Navidades pasadas, fui a Sierra Nevada, en Granada, con mi familia. Visitamos los mercados navideños de la ciudad, donde había luces preciosas, adornos y recuerdos fabricados en la región.
Después, la mañana de Navidad, abrimos nuestros regalos y nos fuimos a esquiar. Sin embargo, como yo no sé esquiar, me quedé en el hotel comiendo dulces navideños como el turrón y jugando. Los dulces de Navidad son deliciosos, ¡los como todos los días!

1. Vega visited…   a) a museum   b) markets   c) a castle

2. They went…   a) skiing   b) hiking   c) swimming

3. She didn't ski because…   a) there was no snow   b) she was ill   c) she cannot ski

Higher reading

4. Read this article about festivals in Bolivia, in South America. Then answer the questions in English.

Carnaval de Oruro
En este carnaval en la ciudad de Oruro, miles de personas bailan y cantan en un desfile que va hasta un santuario*. Durante esta peregrinación**, las personas llevan máscaras y trajes muy coloridos. En el santuario, se quitan esas máscaras y rezan a la Virgen.

Festival Internacional de Cine de Santa Cruz (FENAVID)
Cada año se celebra en Santa Cruz este festival de cine, uno de los más importantes de América Latina. Los participantes pueden ver más de 150 producciones audiovisuales como películas, cortos y vídeos musicales, de todo el mundo. Los asistentes deben reservar su hotel con antelación, ya que hay muchos visitantes en la ciudad durante el festival.

San Juan
Tradicionalmente, los bolivianos celebran esta fiesta religiosa quemando los elementos que no quieren en sus vidas. Sin embargo, hoy es más común celebrar San Juan con fuegos artificiales y barbacoas en las que toda la comunidad participa. La gente también celebra esta fiesta bailando y cantando en la calle.

* El santuario = Shrine
** La peregrinación = Pilgrimage

---

a. What is Oruro? _____

b. Where do participants go during Oruro's Carnival? _____

c. Where do the movies at FENAVID come from? _____

d. What are tourists advised to do? Why? _____

e. How would you translate "quemando" here? _____

f. What has changed in the celebration of San Juan? _____

5. Read what Rodrigo has to say about traditional marriage in Spain. Complete the sentences.

La boda tradicional española es una boda católica y dura un día. La novia viste un traje blanco caro y bonito y el novio lleva traje.

Antes normalmente había un compromiso antes de la boda. El futuro marido, acompañado de sus padres, pedía permiso a los padres de la novia para casarse con ella. A veces, solo los padres del novio y de la novia participaban en este compromiso.

En la actualidad, muchas bodas son civiles, no religiosas y pueden durar varios días. A menudo hay una primera celebración para la familia más cercana y luego una segunda fiesta con todos los amigos de los novios.

a. Weddings in the past lasted _____

b. The bride wears _____

c. The husband-to-be asked _____

d. Nowadays, many weddings are _____, last _____ and have _____

Higher reading

6. Read this article from a website about customs in rural Spain, then answer the questions in English.

Si te invitan a quedarte con una familia en un pueblo pequeño o rural, no dudes en responder a todas las preguntas que te hagan. ¿Cuántos hijos tienes?, ¿cuántos años tienes?, ¿de qué trabajas?

Después de comer, cuando hace mucho sol y calor, muchas personas duermen la siesta o ven la televisión en el sofá. Las tiendas están cerradas y no hay nadie en la calle.

Sin embargo, cuando el sol ha caído y no hace mucho calor, muchas personas sacan una silla a la calle, enfrente de sus casas, y se sientan a hablar con los vecinos. Es también muy común ir a la plaza del pueblo para ver y hablar con las demás personas del pueblo.

Si dos personas caminan de la mano son pareja. Los amigos nunca se dan la mano para caminar. Los matrimonios y bautismos de bebés son dos de las celebraciones más importantes en los pueblos en España.

a. What is the first piece of advice given? _____

b. What THREE examples of this are given? _____
_____

c. What do you do after lunch? Mention two things.
_____

d. When do people go to the town's plaza? _____

e. When two people hold hands, what is this a sign of? _____

f. What do you think a *bautismo* is? _____

7. Read what Liliana says about her beliefs.

Cuando era joven, era bastante religiosa, iba a la iglesia todos los domingos y creía en Dios. Hace cinco años dejé de creer, pero sigo yendo a la iglesia de vez en cuando, como cuando nace un niño y hay un bautizo. De hecho, voy a asistir a la boda de mi hermana dentro de tres meses.

a. How have Liliana's beliefs changed? Mention two points.
_____

b. When does she go to church? _____

c. What will happen in three months? _____

Grammar focus
The Present Tense

Below are examples of the present tense in use.

Yo celebro mi cumpleaños todos los años.	I **celebrate** my birthday every year.
Tú celebras tu cumpleaños en enero.	You **celebrate** your birthday in January.
Nosotros celebramos la Navidad en diciembre.	We **celebrate** Christmas in December.
Ellos celebran su aniversario de bodas.	They **celebrate** their wedding anniversary.

Notice the endings on the verb *celebrar* in español. *Celebrar* is the **infinitive** (to celebrate), but in the present tense you have to remove the "-ar" from the infinitive and add endings to the stem that is left. *Celebrar* is a regular verb. As we'll see, many common verbs are not regular.

Noticing the present tense

Translate each sentence below. Indicate whether it is PRESENT (PRES), PAST or FUTURE (FUT) then translate the sentence as in the example.

Ejemplo: Yo recibo un montón de regalos.	PRES	I receive a lot of presents.
He recibido tres regalos de cumpleaños.		
Normalmente celebro la Pascua en abril.		
Ayer celebré mi cumpleaños.		
Fuimos al festival de ciencia.		
Siempre hago regalos.		
Mi madre me ha hecho un regalo precioso.		
Mis amigos van a una fiesta mañana.		
Vamos a la sinagoga muy a menudo.		
Me encanta hacer celebraciones con mis amigos.		
A mis padres les encantaba celebrar la Navidad.		
Mis amigos van a ir a un festival el próximo sábado.		
He ido a la sinagoga con mis padres.		
Yo voy a la mezquita a rezar.		
El festival fue fantástico.		

The Present Tense

Regular verbs		
- AR verbs	**-ER verbs**	**-IR verbs**
Celebrar - *to change*	**Creer** - *to believe*	**Descubrir** - *to discover*
Yo celebr**o**	Yo cre**o**	Yo descubr**o**
Tú celebr**as**	Tú cre**es**	Tú descubr**es**
Él/ella/usted celebr**a**	Él/ella/usted cre**e**	Él/ella/usted descubr**e**
Nosotros celebr**amos**	Nosotros cre**emos**	Nosotros descubr**imos**
Vosotros celebr**áis**	Vosotros cre**éis**	Vosotros descubr**ís**
Ellos/ustedes celebr**an**	Ellos/ustedes cre**en**	Ellos/ustedes descubr**en**

Key Irregular verbs

*Estar *to be*	Yo estoy… *I am*	**Saber** *to know*	Yo sé… *I know*
Hacer *to do*	Yo hago… *I do*	**Salir** *to go out*	Yo salgo … *I go out*
Ir *to go*	Yo voy… *I go*	***Ser** *to be*	Yo soy… *I am*
Poder *to be able to*	Yo puedo … *I can*	**Tener** *to have*	Yo tengo… *I have*
Poner *to put*	Yo pongo… *I put*	**Venir** *to come*	Yo vengo… *I come*

*Ser and **Estar** both mean *"to be"*. **Ser** is used for physical & character descriptions, e.g. **soy alto/inteligente** *I am tall/smart* and **Estar** is used for <u>states</u> of wellbeing/emotions, e.g. **estoy en forma** *I am in shape* or **estoy contento/a** *I am happy.*

---

1. Match up.

Recibir	To wish
Desear	To offer
Celebrar	To receive
Querer	To go out
Dar	To see
Ver	To want
Conocer	To give
Salir	To visit
Creer	To believe
Ofrecer	To meet
Visitar	To celebrate
Tomar	To buy
Comprar	To fast
Ayunar	To take

2. Complete with a suitable option.

a. _____ regalos a mis familiares.

b. _____ a mis abuelos.

c. _____ el desfile del Día Nacional.

d. _____ salir con mis primos.

e. _____ marisco.

f. _____ con mis amigos por la ciudad.

g. _____ la Navidad en mi casa con una gran comida.

h. _____ en Dios.

Creo	**Quiero**	**Veo**	**Salgo**
Compro	**Celebro**	**Visito**	**Como**

---

3. Circle the correct form of the verb.

a. Vender: yo vendo/vende

b. Recibir: tú recibo/recibes

c. Celebrar: usted celebras/celebra

d. Creer: nosotros creemos/creéis

e. Ofrecer: yo ofrezco/ofrece

f. Engordar: él engorda/engordáis

g. Elegir: vosotros elegís/eligen

h. Tomar: ustedes toma/toman

i. Regalar: usted regalas/regala

j. Salir: nosotros salimos/salís

k. Visitar: ellos visitáis/visitan

l. Comprar: tú compras/compra

m. Asistir: vosotros asistís/asiste

n. Deber: usted debe/deben

4. Translate into English.

a. Yo recibo _____

b. Tú visitas _____

c. Ustedes ofrecen

_____

d. Vosotros celebráis

_____

e. Él elige _____

f. Usted sale _____

5. Add the missing letters.

a. Po _ _ _ _ _ (we put)

b. V _ (she goes)

c. Ha _ _ _ _ _ (we do)

d. Ve _ _ _ (I come)

e. El _ _ _ _ (you sing. choose)

f. Te _ _ _ _ _ _ _ _ (we finish)

g. Es _ _ _ _ _ (they wait)

h. ¿Qué ha _ _ _? (you sing. do)

i. En _ _ _ _ _ (I put on weight)

j. Vi _ _ _ _ _ _ (you plural visit)

k. Com _ _ _ (you formal, sing. buy)

l. Co _ _ (I eat)

6. Complete with a suitable verb.

a. Usted c_____ dulces.

b. Nosotros v_____ a la iglesia.

c. Él v_____ a sus amigos.

d. Tú r_____ regalos.

e. Yo s_____ de casa.

f. Ustedes c_____ la Navidad.

g. Vosotros c_____ regalos.

7. Insert *Yo, Tú, Ella, Nosotros, Vosotros o Ellos* as appropriate.

a. _____ vamos a ponernos un traje.

b. _____ reciben regalos

c. _____ como muchos pasteles.

d. ¿Qué hacen _____ en Navidad?

e. _____ celebráis Yom Kippur.

f. Durante Eid _____ ayuna

g. En Navidad_____ comemos mucho.

h. _____ no cree en Dios.

i. _____ no quieren regalos.

j. _____ bebéis mucho cava.

k. _____ voy a casa en Nochebuena.

l. _____ van a pasar las vacaciones en Cuba.

m. _____ va a la sinagoga con sus padres.

n. _____ nos quedamos en casa.

o. ¿ Visita _____ a sus padres?

p. ¿ _____ ves a tus primos?

8. Translate into Spanish.

a. We put _____

b. I go _____

c. She waits _____

d. They visit _____

e. We eat _____

f. They fast _____

g. We receive _____

h. I take _____

i. She wants _____

j. I pray _____

k. Do you see? _____

l. We celebrate _____

m. I watch _____

n. They give _____

o. I believe _____

9. Translate into Spanish (easier).

a. They (F) go to church.

b. She goes out a lot.

c. We stay at home.

d. They (M) eat seafood.

e. I receive some gifts.

f. We celebrate at home.

g. Do you believe in God?

h. I always watch the procession.

i. We pray and fast.

10. Translate into Spanish (harder).

a. At Christmas we give and receive a lot of presents.

b. I never go to big music festivals.

c. They celebrate Easter at home.

d. I believe that it's important to maintain traditions.

e. We want to go to the Diwali Festival next week.

f. After giving presents, we usually eat together.

g. The city organises a festival every year.

h. Every year we go to see the Easter parade.

i. I have just bought a present for my friend.

j. Valentine's Day is the tradition that I like least.

Preparing for speaking and writing

1. Match up.

Yo celebro	I stay
Yo doy	I celebrate
Yo como	I see
Yo voy	I congratulate
Yo descanso	I give
Yo disfruto	I discover
Yo felicito	I eat
Yo descubro	I enjoy
Yo veo	I meet up with
Yo quedo con	I fast
Yo recibo	I rest
Yo me quedo	I receive
Yo ayuno	I go

2. Complete with a suitable verb from activity 1.

a. En casa _____ la Navidad pero no la Pascua.

b. _____ a mis familiares.

c. _____ en mi casa.

d. _____ de las vacaciones.

e. _____ en casa de mis abuelos.

f. _____ pavo.

g. _____ una semana a Costa Rica.

h. _____ y recibo regalos.

3. Anagrams.

a. us dsoi   [their god]   _____

b. uan faseti   [a festival]   _____

c. ne andavid   [at Christmas]   _____

d. oy yov   [I go]   _____

e. ne mi saca   [at my house]   _____

f. nostorso magostas [we spend]   _____

g. le prxóoim envaro [next summer]   _____

h. ne acapus   [at Easter]   _____

i. nu alegro   [a gift]   _____

j. nua piconerós [a procession]   _____

k. nua rgna cadmio [a big meal]   _____

l. esfugo facilitareis [fireworks]   _____

4. Broken words.

a. Du _ _ _ _ _   [during]

b. Fi_ _ _ _   [party]

c. Yo ga _ _ _   [I spend]

d. En mi c_ _ _ _   [at my house]

e. Con mi fam_ _ _ _   [with my family]

f. Nosotros v_ _ _ _   [we see]

g. Yo qu_ _ _   [I meet]

h. Ce _ _ _ _ _ _ _ _   [we celebrate]

5. Complete the table.

Infinitive	Present	Perfect Tense
Pasar	Yo paso	Yo he pasado
Ir		
Descansar		
Dar		
Disfrutar		
Ver		
Celebrar		
Recibir		

6. Complete the translation.

a. I spend the Christmas holidays at home.   Yo p_ _ _   las vacaciones de Navidad en mi c_ _ _.

b. At Easter, I go to church.   En P _ _ _ _ _ voy a la i_ _ _ _ _ _.

c. There are fireworks and a long procession.   Hay f _ _ _ _ _ artificiales y una gran p_ _ _ _ _ _ _ _.

d. I usually go to the mosque to pray.   Normalmente voy a la m_ _ _ _ _ _ _ para r_ _ _ _.

e. We offer and receive gifts.   Nosotros d_ _ _ _ y r_ _ _ _ _ _ _ _ r_ _ _ _ _ _.

f. Yom Kippur is a Jewish festival.   Yom Kippur es una f_ _ _ _ _ j_ _ _ _.

g. Our relatives gather at our house.   Nuestros f_ _ _ _ _ _ _ _ se reúnen en n_ _ _ _ _ _ casa.

---

7. Add the missing accents.

a. Vosotros celebrais.

b. Las ultimas vacaciones.

c. Musulman.

d. Una fiesta judia.

e. Una celebracion religiosa.

f. Catolico.

g. Una tradicion española.

h. El Dia de la Madre.

i. El Roscon de Reyes

8. Sentence puzzle – put the words in the right order.

a. fiesta una es Eid musulmana: _____

b. desfiles A hay menudo: _____

c. comemos Nosotros navideños dulces: _____

d. y Yo doy regalos recibo: _____

e. es Navidad favorita Mi fiesta: _____

f. regalos gente La compra: _____

g. veo y a Yo amigos mis familiares: _____

---

9. Translate into Spanish (easier).

a. I go to church with my parents.

b. We receive some gifts.

c. There are fireworks in the park.

d. I celebrate Eid with my family.

e. We celebrate Christmas every year.

f. I visit my grandparents at Easter.

g. I spend Easter at home in April.

h. I eat lots of Christmas sweets.

i. I fast and pray at the mosque.

j. My relatives gather at my house.

k. I celebrate Yom Kippur with my family.

l. My favorite festival is Diwali.

---

10. Translate into Spanish (harder).

a. At Christmas my friends and relatives gather at my house to celebrate together.

b. In many villages in Spain, there are processions and fireworks to celebrate this festival.

c. It is my favourite festival because I receive lots of gifts from my parents and relatives.

d. I usually don't go anywhere during the holidays. I stay at home, watch TV and eat a lot.

e. I love national holidays because we don't have to go to school and do homework.

f. In my region there are a lot of things to see so during the holidays we go out a lot.

g. During this festival I fast, go to the mosque and pray.

Speaking in a role-play

Look at the instructions on the left as they would appear in a speaking test. Read aloud with a partner the dialogue on the right. Then do the dialogue a second time, changing the answers in bold. Take turns playing the two roles.

Foundation (Where you see ..., your partner makes up a short reply).

1. Say when your birthday is.
2. Say one thing you do on your birthday.
3. Ask your friend a question about marriage.
4. Describe a present you received for your last birthday (give one detail).
5. Say what you think about traditions (give one detail).

1. ¿Cuándo es tu cumpleaños?
   El 29 de enero.

2. ¿Y cómo lo celebras?
   Preparo una fiesta con mis amigos.

3. ¿Crees que el matrimonio es importante?
   ...

4. ¿Qué te regalaron en tu último cumpleaños?
   Una entrada de cine.

5. ¿Cuál es tu opinión sobre las tradiciones?
   Creo que son importantes.

....

Higher (Where you see ..., your partner makes up a short reply).

1. Describe a festival you have attended (give one detail and one opinion).
2. Describe what you did at Easter (give two details).
3. Ask your friend a question about last Christmas.
4. Mention two things there are for tourists in your region.
5. Say what you plan to do in the summer (give two details).

1. ¿Has ido a algún festival?
   Sí, fui a un festival de cocina. Fue muy interesante.

2. ¿Qué hiciste en Semana Santa?
   Comí mucho chocolate y fui a ver a mis abuelos.

3. ¿Qué hiciste en Navidad?
   ...

4. ¿Qué pueden ver los turistas en tu región?
   Pueden visitar castillos y hacer senderismo.

5. ¿Qué vas a hacer el verano que viene?
   Me voy de vacaciones a España con mis padres.

Writing and speaking from a photo card

Write something about each of these photos. Write about who you see, where they are what they are doing. Read out your description.

_____   _____

_____   _____

_____   _____

Answer the following questions related to this topic. Read out your answers.

1. ¿Cuál es tu fiesta favorita del año?

_____

_____

2. ¿Cómo sueles celebrar tu cumpleaños?

_____

_____

3. Habla de un festival en tu región.

_____

_____

_____

4. ¿Qué hiciste durante las últimas vacaciones?

_____

_____

_____

5. ¿Qué vas a hacer el próximo fin de semana?

_____

_____

Foundation writing

Write about 50 words in Spanish. Write something about each point.

• Your birthday   • How old you are   • How you celebrate it   • Presents you like   • A favourite present

1. _____

2. _____

3. _____

4. _____

5. _____

Using your knowledge of grammar complete the sentences below, choosing one of the three options given.

1.   Mi cumpleaños _____ el cinco de mayo (es/son/tiene).

2.   Nosotros _____ a un festival de cine (vamos/vais/van).

3.   El sábado pasado fui a _____ un castillo histórico (veo/visto /ver).

4.   Es una tradición _____ (histórico/histórica/históricas).

5.   Yo _____ Diwali con mi familia (celebro/celebras/celebra).

Foundation/Higher writing

Write approximately 90 words in Spanish. You must refer to each bullet point.

• An interesting festival   • A recent celebration   • Plans for the summer

_____

_____

_____

_____

_____

_____

_____

Higher writing

Write approximately 150 words in Spanish about both bullet points. You can either refer to the language in this unit, for example the sentence bank, or do the task in "exam conditions," without help. Or you could do both!

• The positive and negative aspects of cultural traditions
• A cultural event you attended recently.

Foundation sentence bank

En mi ciudad hay una mezquita y una catedral.	There is a mosque and a cathedral in my city.
La Navidad es una gran tradición familiar para nosotros.	Christmas is a great family tradition at our house.
En Pascua comemos mucho chocolate.	At Easter, we eat a lot of chocolate.
Todos los años hay un festival de música.	There is a music festival every year.
Recibo regalos por mi cumpleaños.	I receive presents for my birthday.
Voy a la sinagoga de vez en cuando.	I go to the synagogue occasionally.
En mi región hay muchos mercados.	In my region there are lots of markets.
Celebramos Eid todos los años	We celebrate Eid each year.
Siempre hago una fiesta de cumpleaños.	I always have a party for my birthday.
Recibí muchos regalos en Navidad.	I received a lot of presents at Christmas.
Voy a celebrar mi cumpleaños con mis amigos.	I am going to celebrate my birthday with my friends.
Compré un regalo para mi madre.	I bought a present for my mother.
Fui al festival de música de Glastonbury.	I went to the Glastonbury music festival.
Creo que las tradiciones son importantes.	I think that traditions are important.

Higher sentence bank

Celebro la Navidad haciendo regalos.	I celebrate Christmas by buying presents.
Acabo de estar en un gran festival de música.	I've just been to a big music festival.
Si fuera más religioso, iría mucho a la iglesia.	If I were more religious, I would go to church often.
Nunca celebramos la Pascua en casa.	We never celebrate Easter at home.
Creo que es importante mantener vivas las tradiciones.	In my opinion it's important to maintain traditions.
Espero ir al festival de cine en octubre.	I hope to go to the film festival in October.
La Navidad es mi fiesta favorita. Me encanta.	Christmas is the festival that I prefer. I love it.
Después de darnos los regalos, tuvimos una gran comida.	After giving presents, we had a big meal.
El año que viene iré al Festival de Leeds.	I shall go to Leeds Festival next year.
Todos los años organizan una fiesta en el pueblo.	They organise a village party every year.
Todos los años hay un gran desfile en la ciudad.	There is a large parade in the town every year.
El año pasado asistí a los Juegos Olímpicos.	I went to the Olympic Games last year.
San Valentín es la tradición que menos me gusta.	Valentine's Day is the tradition that I like least.
Creo que el matrimonio es una tradición importante.	I believe that marriage is an important tradition.

UNIT 5

Media and technology

Contents

- **Foundation vocab building.**
- **Foundation reading.**
- **Higher vocab building.**
- **Higher reading.**
- **Grammar focus – the Perfect Tense.**
- **Preparing for speaking and writing.**
- **Writing and speaking from a photo card.**
- **Speaking in a role play.**
- **Writing.**
- **Sentence bank.**

Foundation vocab building

Vocabulary

bajar/descargar	to download
caro	expensive
charlar	to chat
compartir	to share
comprar	to buy
conectado	connected
digital	digital
disminuir	to decrease
disponible	available
el dispositivo	device
en línea	online
enviar	to send
escuchar	to listen
fabricar	to manufacture
la foto	photo
la generación	generation
grabar	to record
gratis	free (of charge)
la herramienta	tool
la informática	IT
joven	young
el juego	game
jugar	to play
la juventud	youth
la llave	key
la luz	light
el mensaje	message
mola	it's cool
el móvil	mobile phone
navegar	to surf/browse
el ordenador	computer
la palabra	word
la pantalla	screen
el programa	programme
preocupante	worrying
publicar	to post/publish
rápido	fast
recibir	to receive
el recibo	receipt
la red	network
robar	to steal
la salud	health
seguir	to follow
seguro	safe
la seguridad	safety
subir	to upload
el texto	text
trabajar	to work
traducir	to translate
usar	to use

1. Match up.

Red	Screen
Juego	To download
Publicar	Available
Móvil	To steal
Ordenador	New
Preocupante	Online
Comprar	Worrying
Nuevo	Programme
Herramienta	Computer
Disponible	Mobile phone
En línea	Network
Descargar	To buy
Pantalla	Tool
Programa	Youth
Robar	Game
Juventud	To upload
Subir	To post

2. Translate into English.

a. Ordenador _____

b. Herramienta _____

c. Pantalla _____

d. Nuevo _____

e. Red _____

f. Juego _____

g. Programa _____

h. Seguir _____

i. Móvil _____

j. Compartir _____

k. Palabra _____

l. Seguro _____

m. Enviar _____

n. Digital _____

3. Anagrams.

e.g. redorando: ordenador

a. ahitarmeren: h_ _ _ _ _ _ _ _ _

b. ejugo: j_ _ _ _

c. cmprora: c _ _ _ _ _ _

d. sirgeu: s_ _ _ _ _

e. busir: s_ _ _ _

f. onidispble: d_ _ _ _ _ _ _ _ _

g. aabrrg: g_ _ _ _ _

h. alplanta: p_ _ _ _ _ _ _

i. nouve: n_ _ _ _

4. Spot and correct the faulty English translations.

a. Las redes sociales: Social problems.

b. Los juegos en línea: Digital games.

c. Una herramienta digital: A digital platform.

d. Un ordenador nuevo: A new mobile phone.

e. Mi móvil viejo: My old TV.

f. Comprar equipos digitales: To sell digital devices.

g. Un programa de televisión nuevo: A new piece of software.

h. Una pantalla nueva: A new mobile phone.

i. Mantenerse conectado: To get connected.

j. Compartir fotos: To take photos.

k. Descargar un programa: To watch a programme.

l. Un problema preocupante: A difficult problem.

5. Break the flow: rewrite the sentences below with the correct gaps in between the words.

a. Esmásrápido [it is faster]: *Es más rápido*

b. Yonavegoporinternet [I go on the internet]: _____

c. Yosigoaalgunosinfluencers [I follow some influencers]: _____

d. CompartofotosenInstagram [I share photos on Instagram]: _____

e. Unpeligrodeinternet [a danger of the internet]: _____

f. Esmásfácilcomunicarse [it is easier to communicate]: _____

g. Pasounmontóndetiempo [I spend a lot of time]: _____

h. Enmimóvilyenmiordenador [on my mobile phone and PC]: _____

---

6. Split words.

me-	-talla	=screen
re-	-moria	= (USB) stick
com-	-cil	= easy
su-	-des	= networks
pan-	-cionar	= to work
fá-	-partir	= to share
fun-	-go	= game
ro-	-guir	= to follow
se-	-bar	= to steal
jue-	-bir	= to upload

---

7. Put the words in the sentences below in the correct order.

a. móvil un tengo nuevo Yo.

_____

b. más comunicarse Es fácil.

_____

c. comparto en Instagram Yo fotos menudo a.

_____

d. los a días internet Yo me conecto todos.

_____

e. Hay peligros internet en muchos.

_____

---

8. Translate into English.

a. En mi móvil.

_____

b. Yo paso un montón de tiempo.

_____

c. Me encanta chatear.

_____

d. Comparto fotos.

_____

e. Voy a comprar.

_____

f. Escucho algunas canciones.

_____

g. Las redes sociales.

_____

h. Envío SMS.

_____

---

9. Translate into English.

a. Instagram es mi red social favorita.

b. Comparto muchas fotos en Facebook.

c. Me encanta chatear con mis amigos en línea.

d. Uno de los peligros de internet es el robo de la identidad.

e. Ayer yo subí un vídeo a YouTube.

f. Yo paso un montón de tiempo en mi ordenador.

g. Siempre hago todos mis deberes con el ordenador.

h. Mañana voy a comprar una memoria USB.

i. Las redes sociales son adictivas.

j. Sigo a varios influencers en TikTok porque son divertidos.

k. No me gusta Facebook. No mola.

l. Me encanta ver vídeos en YouTube.

Foundation reading

1. Read what three young people say about phones.

Paula

Paso mucho tiempo con el móvil. Me encanta hacerme muchos selfies. Eso sí, nunca envío correos electrónicos.

Juan

No uso mucho el móvil. Prefiero hablar con mis amigos en persona. Me gusta estar con la gente.

Raúl

Utilizo el móvil principalmente para estar en contacto con mi familia y amigos y para buscar información en internet.

Who says what? Put a cross in the correct box.

Who...	Paula	Juan	Raúl
a. ...doesn't use their phone much?			
b. ...looks up things online?			
c. ...spends lots of time on their phone?			
d. ...mainly uses their phone to keep in touch?			
e. ...never sends emails?			
f. ...prefers being with people in person?			

2. Read what these young people say about social media.

Carla

Creo que la gente pasa demasiado tiempo en las redes sociales. No es bueno para su salud mental o felicidad.

Valeria

En mi opinión, las redes sociales son una forma estupenda de mantener el contacto con los amigos.

Pablo

Hay que tener cuidado con la seguridad en internet. Yo nunca doy mis datos personales.

Circle the correct answer.

1. Carla thinks social media makes people...   (a) lazy   (b) unhappy   (c) unsociable

2. Valeria thinks social media encourages...   (a) communication   (b) isolation   (c) time-wasting

3. Pablo thinks social media can be...   (a) addictive   (b) unsafe   (c) fun

Foundation reading

3. These people mention their favourite apps.

Emma
Tengo una aplicación con información práctica de salud por si tienes un problema urgente. Está muy bien.

Sergio
Tengo una aplicación que me da información actualizada sobre el tiempo.

Carmen
Mi aplicación favorita me dice qué canción estoy escuchando. ¡Me encanta!

David
Me gusta la aplicación que permite compartir el coche con otras personas.

Which person has the following app?

a. A car sharing app _____

b. An app which gives medical information _____

c. An app which can tell you what song you are listening to. _____

d. An app with the latest weather alerts. _____

4. Read this description of an app called Entourage. Then answer the questions in English.

Entourage es una nueva aplicación muy útil porque pone en contacto a la gente. Quien que necesite algo (ropa, alojamiento, una charla, un café) puede ponerse en contacto con otras personas que estén cerca y que puedan ayudarles. Entourage también ha creado una sencilla guía para conocer gente en la calle. Desde que se creó la aplicación, 1.000 personas han podido conectar, ¡eso está muy bien!

---

a. What does the Entourage app do? _____

b. Mention two things people might need. (i) _____ (ii) _____

c. What does their guide help with? _____

d. What happened after the app was created? _____

5. Fernando describes how her media habits have changed.

Leo el periódico en papel todos los días. Cuando era más joven también veía mucho la televisión y utilizaba internet para conocer las noticias. Sin embargo, ahora no me gusta la televisión tradicional, así que voy a comprar una plataforma de streaming con canales de información 24 horas.

After each item, mark whether it refers to the Past (P), Now (N) or the Future (F).

a. Reading a traditional newspaper _____

b. Watching TV _____

c. Subscribing to a streaming platform _____

Foundation reading

6. Tomás describes how he uses his computer.

> El ordenador es muy importante para mí porque lo uso para hacer los deberes. También me gusta comprar cosas por internet, como ropa o regalos para mis amigos y familiares.
>
> Además, me interesa la inteligencia artificial. Por ejemplo, me encanta crear imágenes para compartirlas con mis amigos. He creado una imagen divertida con animales en un planeta.
>
> Por último, a veces veo series en línea o vídeos en YouTube. Mis vídeos favoritos son cortometrajes sobre los últimos dispositivos electrónicos.

Tick any of these activities which Tomás uses his computer for.

a) watching videos ☐   b) creating pictures ☐   c) social media ☐   d) web design ☐

e) playing games ☐   f) doing homework ☐   g) email ☐   h) shopping ☐

7. Leila gives her opinion about social media.

> ¡Me encanta mi móvil! Hago fotos y vídeos y los comparto con mis amigas. También recibo y envío muchos mensajes por WhatsApp, pero nunca entro en TikTok o X. Tampoco hago los deberes en el ordenador.
> Lo malo es que es cierto que paso demasiado tiempo con el móvil, como muchos adolescentes. Sin embargo, creo que las redes sociales son buenas para la gente que está sola, por ejemplo, las personas mayores.

In the boxes, tick three things Leila says.

a) I share photos with friends. ☐   d) Social media makes people feel less alone. ☐

b) I shop online. ☐   e) I receive and send messages on WhatsApp. ☐

c) I do my homework. ☐   f) I don't spend a lot of time on my phone. ☐

8. César explains what he doesn't do to protect his online safety. Answer the question in English.

> Para estar seguro, nunca comparto mis contraseñas*. No descargo programas que no conozco y no compro nada en línea en una wifi pública.
>
> * contraseña = password

Describe the three things César says.

a) _____

b) _____

c) _____

Higher vocab building

Vocabulary

actual	current
bajar/descargar	to download
caro	expensive
compartir	to share
la compra	shopping
comprar	to buy
conectado	connected
emitir	to broadcast
encender	to turn on
enviar	to send
fabricar	to manufacture
digital	digital
disponible	available
dispositivo	device
enlace	link
la generación	generation
grabar	to record
gratis	free (of charge)
la herramienta	tool
la informática	IT
joven	young
el juego	game
jugar	to play
la juventud	youth
la memoria USB	USB stick
la luz	light
la marca	brand
el mensaje de texto	SMS
el móvil	mobile phone
el ordenador	computer
la palabra	word
la pantalla	screen
el poder	power
poderoso	powerful
preocupante	worrying
el programa	programme
recibir	to receive
el recibo	receipt
la red	network
robar	to steal
en línea	online
la salud	health
la seguridad	safety
seguir	to follow
seguro	safe
trabajar	to work
traducir	to translate
usar	to use

1. Match up.

Enviar	To record
Encender	To download
Emitir	To send
Grabar	To translate
Descargar	To play
Traducir	To turn on
Reproducir	To read
Leer	To watch
Ver	To broadcast
Recibir	To follow
Seguir	To receive
Apagar	To buy
Comprar	To turn off

2. Complete with the correct option.

a. _____ un SMS.

b. _____ la televisión.

c. _____ a videojuegos en mi móvil.

d. _____ la luz.

e. _____ compras en línea.

f. _____ influencer.

g. _____ fotos en Instagram.

h. _____ un ordenador nuevo.

Veo	Compro	Comparto	Soy
Hago	Envío	Juego	Enciendo

3. Spot and correct the errors in the English translations below.

a. Me gusta jugar con el ordenador: I like to play on my mobile phone.

b. Apago el ordenador: I turn on my computer.

c. A menudo me conecto a internet: I occasionally connect to the internet.

d. Comparto fotos en Instagram: I like photos on Instagram.

e. Sigo a algunos influencers: I like some influencers.

f. Le envío muchos correos: I receive many emails from him.

g. Es una buena herramienta digital: It's a good digital platform.

h. Ya no está disponible en línea: It is no longer available in the shops.

i. Soy adicto a mi móvil: I am addicted to my tablet.

4. Split sentences.

Juego y trabajo con (1)	de deporte y música.
Mi tema favorito es	vídeos en Facebook.
internet es peligroso debido	mi ordenador. (1)
Hago muchas fotos	herramienta útil.
Sigo programas de televisión	al robo de identidad.
Me gusta compartir	tema preocupante.
WordReference es una	la informática.
El robo de identidad es un	de ordenador favorita.
Apple es mi marca	son peligrosas.
Creo que las redes sociales	con mi móvil.

5. Gapped translation.

a. El impacto de la tecnología digital es positivo: The impact of _____ technology is positive.

b. Acabo de comprar un ordenador nuevo: I have _____ bought a new computer.

c. Yo no compro nada en línea: I don't buy _____ online.

d. Ya no utilizo más las redes sociales: I don't use _____ any longer.

e. Lo que me preocupa es el acoso en línea: What _____ me is online bullying.

f. El robo de identidad es muy común hoy en día: Identity _____ is very common these days.

g. Nadie puede predecir el futuro de la inteligencia artificial: Nobody can predict the _____ of AI.

h. He aprendido mucho buscando en internet: I have learnt a lot by _____ the web.

i. Rara vez descargo música: I rarely _____ music.

j. No compartiré más mis datos personales: I shall no longer _____ my personal data.

k. No debes creer todo lo que lees: You must not believe everything you _____.

l. Usar las redes sociales nos hace estar menos aislados: By using social media we are _____ isolated.

6. Match the opposites.

Enciendo	Yo recibo
Caro	Difícil
Seguro	Apago
Yo envío	Barato
Fácil	Yo vendo
Actual	Peligroso
Yo compro	Todo
Nada	Pasado
Joven	Aumentar
Disminuir	Viejo

7. One of three. Circle the right translation.

Seguro	Silly	Unsafe	Safe
Funcionar	To send	To work	To broadcast
Actual	Past	Actual	Current
Encender	To turn on	To turn off	To break
Joven	Expensive	Young	Old
Disponible	Available	Disposable	Impossible
Robar	To power up	To break	To steal
Enviar	To send	To receive	To find
Palabra	Text	Word	Screen
Compra	Purchase	Network	Money

8. Translate into English.

a. Las compras en línea.

b. Encender el ordenador.

c. Comprar un móvil.

d. Adictos a las redes sociales

e. Enviar mensajes de texto.

f. Palabras ofensivas.

9. Translate into English.

a. Muchos jóvenes son adictos a las redes sociales hoy en día.

b. Los adolescentes pasan mucho tiempo en internet.

c. Lo preocupante es que el robo de identidad es muy común.

d. Internet no es un lugar seguro. Hay muchos peligros.

e. El teléfono móvil es un poderoso medio de comunicación.

f. Las nuevas tecnologías facilitan la comunicación.

g. Gracias a internet podemos comprar y jugar en línea.

h. Podemos mantenernos en contacto con personas que viven lejos.

i. Aprendo mucho buscando información en línea.

j. Ya nunca uso las redes sociales.

Higher reading

1. Read this description of a helpful app. Then answer the questions in English.

La aplicación TOM Recordatorio de Medicamentos es útil para las personas mayores que tienen dificultades para recordar las cosas. Avisa a los usuarios de que es hora de tomar su medicación. Ellos pueden programar las horas a las que el móvil les avisa de que deben tomar el medicamento.

Otra ventaja útil es que la aplicación te puede recordar si has tomado o no la medicación. Hay otras aplicaciones como esta. Es un buen ejemplo de tecnología que ayuda a las personas en su vida cotidiana.

a.   Who is this app for exactly? _____

b.   What does it do? _____

c.   What is another practical use referred to in the description? _____

_____

d.   What does the final sentence say? _____

_____

2.   Read this article about positive uses for Artificial Intelligence ("inteligencia artificial" or IA in Spanish). Then answer the questions in English.

La IA puede ayudar a las personas con discapacidad. Una empresa la ha utilizado la IA para crear StorySign, una aplicación móvil gratuita que ayuda a los niños que no pueden ver. La aplicación traduce textos escritos al lenguaje de signos. La misma empresa también ha creado Track AI, un dispositivo de bajo coste y fácil uso que identifica problemas en niños con problemas para escuchar. Este dispositivo sugiere un posible tratamiento.

Otra aplicación es Facing Emotions, que traduce las emociones en sonidos cortos para ayudar a las personas con discapacidad visual a "ver" las emociones de los demás. La aplicación utiliza la cámara de los móviles para analizar la posición de la nariz, la boca y los ojos de la otra persona. Con esta información, la IA puede identificar la expresión facial y la emoción correspondiente, como miedo, alegría o sorpresa.

a.   Who is StorySign for? _____

b.   What does StorySign do? _____

c.   How much does StorySign cost? _____

d.   What does Track AI do? Mention two points.
i) _____
ii) _____

e.   Who is Facing Emotions for? _____

f.   Describe what it does. Mention two points.
i) _____
ii) _____

Higher reading

3. Read what these people think about social media.

Mar

Me gusta estar en contacto con los demás a través de las redes sociales. Siempre puedo comunicarme con mis seres queridos en cualquier momento.

Olivia

Ya no uso las redes sociales. Todo lo que veo son discusiones e insultos. ¡Es una pena!

Blanca

La comunicación con los demás me resulta muy útil. Sin embargo, la cantidad de tiempo que paso en las redes sociales me preocupa.

Juan Carlos

Sin las redes sociales estaría mucho más solo, así que nunca me arrepiento de pasar tiempo conectado.

Álex

Prefiero hablar con la gente sin utilizar un móvil. En mi opinión, la gente depende demasiado de esta tecnología.

What do they think about social media? In each box write P for a positive opinion, N for a negative opinion, P + N for a positive and negative opinion.

a. Mar _____   c. Blanca _____   e. Álex _____

b. Olivia _____   d. Juan Carlos _____

4. Read this review by Laura of a new TV series. Then answer the questions in English.

El sábado pasado vi esta serie por primera vez en la plataforma Disney+. Es una serie de ciencia ficción ambientada dentro de dos siglos en un planeta alejado de la Tierra. En esta época, la gente ya no tiene teléfonos inteligentes y puede comunicarse entre sí mediante el pensamiento, sin tener que hablar ni escribir. Esto causa problemas cuando una mujer descubre que su marido va a matar a alguien. Tiene que decidir si se asocia con él.

---

a. When does the story take place? _____

b. Where does the story take place? _____

c. How do people communicate? _____

d. What does the wife have to decide exactly? _____

Higher reading

5. Natalia talks about how she earns her living.

Compro y vendo artículos por internet desde hace cinco años para ganarme la vida. Antes vendía artículos eléctricos, pero ya no lo hago. Ahora vendo sobre todo ropa porque mucha gente prefiere comprar prendas de segunda mano por razones medioambientales. Es mejor reutilizar que consumir. Además, estoy creando mi propio sitio web. Voy a vender artículos, subir vídeos y escribir blogs sobre las últimas ofertas.

What does the article say about these events? Write P for something that happened in the past, N for something that is happening now, F for something that will happen in the future.

a. Buying and selling clothes ☐

b. Buying and selling electricals ☐

c. Uploading videos ☐

d. Creating a website ☐

6. People are giving advice about online habits.

Samuel
Nunca comparto mis contraseñas, ni siquiera con mis padres. Además, sólo compro en sitios conocidos o que he utilizado antes. Por último, evito pinchar en los anuncios.

Clara
Nunca utilizo las mismas contraseñas en dos sitios distintos. Además, prefiero no chatear en internet con gente que no conozco. No sabes con quién te comunicas. Los anuncios están bien. De hecho, me gusta verlos.

Laura
Nunca entro en sitios que no sean seguros. Tampoco descargo programas cuyo origen preciso desconozco.

Who does <u>not</u> do the following things? In the box, write S for Samuel, C for Clara and L for Laura.

a. Talk online with strangers. ☐

b. Download files from an unknown source. ☐

c. Visit insecure websites. ☐

d. Share passwords with anyone. ☐

e. Click on advertisements. ☐

f. Use unfamiliar shopping sites. ☐

Grammar focus: using negatives

Look at the sentences below with their translations in English.

No pincho en los anuncios.	I do **not** click on ads.
Nunca juego a juegos en línea.	I **never** play online games.
Ya no descargo música	I **no longer** download music. (I don't download… **anymore**).
No compro nada en línea.	I buy **nothing** online. (I don't buy **anything**).
No conozco a nadie sin teléfono.	I know **no one** without a phone. (I don't know **anyone**…)
Solo envío SMS.	I **only** send texts.

So, very often, the negative consists of the word **no**, which always goes before the conjugated verb. When we use **nunca**, we may use **no** too or only *nunca* ("nunca juego a juegos en línea").

1. Translate these sentences into English.

a. **No me gustan** los videojuegos.	
b. **Nunca descargo** películas.	
c. **No compro** ropa nueva.	
d. **No vendo nada** en internet.	
e. **Sólo compro** libros.	
f. **No conozco a nadie** en línea.	

When you get two verbs together, e.g. I like to go, I must buy, I want to talk, the "no" goes before the conjugated verb (the first one). The second verb goes in infinitive, participle or -ING form ("gerundio" in Spanish). Sometimes, in between the two verbs, there is a preposition like "a" or "de". This combination of 2 verbs (plus sometimes a preposition too) is called a phrasal verb ("perífrasis verbal").

2. Translate these examples into English.

a. **No me gusta comprar** por internet.	
b. **No voy a ver** esa serie nunca más.	
c. **No debo compartir** mis contraseñas.	
d. **No quiero comprar** un ordenador nuevo.	

If you want to say that something is **no longer** happening, you can use the structure **"ya no"**.
e.g. Antes me gustaba el café, pero **ya no**.   *I used to like coffee, but **not anymore**.*
Ya no estudio español, ahora estudio francés.   *I **don't** study Spanish **anymore**, now I study French.*

3. Translate these examples into English.

a. Antes comía carne, pero **ya no**.	
b. **Ya no** tengo tiempo para ir al gimnasio.	
c. Antes me gustaba la música pop, pero **ya no**.	
d. **Ya no** veo los dibujos animados.	

1. Sentence puzzle – put the words in the right order.

a. con no Yo en línea nadie chateo   [I don't chat with anyone online]

_____

b. amigos no con mis Ya salgo   [I don't go out anymore with my friends]

_____

c. compro No en línea   [I don't do online shopping]

_____

d. uso no Ya las sociales redes   [I don't use social networks anymore]

_____

e. interesante en Creo no que hay nada la tele   [I think that there is nothing interesting on TV]

_____

f. cine mis padres Ya al con no voy   [I don't go to the cinema any longer with my parents]

_____

g. descargo muy No vídeos a menudo   [I don't download videos very often]

_____

h. juego a Nunca videojuegos   [I never play video games]

_____

2. Complete with *no, nunca, nadie, nada* or *ya* as appropriate.

a. _____ juego a la PlayStation.   [I never play on the PlayStation]

b. _____ utilizo mi tarjeta de crédito en línea.   [I don't use my credit card online]

c. No conozco a _____ sin un móvil.   [I don't know anyone without a mobile phone]

d. _____ no uso Facebook.   [I don't go on Facebook any longer]

e. No hay _____ interesante en las redes sociales. [There is nothing interesting on social networks]

f. _____ me sigue en X.   [No one follows me on X]

3. Spot and correct the mistakes.

a. Conozco a nadie sin móvil.

b. No nunca uso internet.

c. Nada juega conmigo.

d. Yo veo nunca series de televisión.

e. No ya uso Snapchat.

f. Tengo no móvil.

g. No nadie chatea conmigo.

h. Yo compro nada por internet.

i. Aun no tengo cuenta en X.

4. Make the sentences below negative using either 'no', 'nunca' or 'ya no' – depending on your own preferences.

e.g. Juego a la PlayStation. *Nunca juego a la PlayStation.*

a. Compro regalos. _____

b. Veo la tele. _____

c. Descargo películas. _____

d. Uso Instagram. _____

e. Sigo a varios influencers. _____

f. Me conecto a menudo. _____

g. Me gustan los programas de telerrealidad. _____

_____

5. Complete the table.

Present Tense	Preterite Tense
e.g. No juego a juegos en línea.	Ayer **jugué** a juegos en línea.
a. Ya no compro por internet.	El fin de semana pasado _____ un libro.
b. Ya no uso Snapchat.	Anoche _____ Snapchat.
c. No chateo en Facebook.	Ayer _____ con mi amigo en Facebook.
d. Nunca bajo películas.	Hace dos días _____ una película de internet.
e. Ya no me conecto a Skype.	El viernes pasado ___ _____ a Skype.
f. No apago el ordenador.	Hoy _____ el ordenador antes de salir de casa.
g. Siempre me meto en Instagram.	Ayer no ___ _____ en Instagram.
h. No comparto nada en las redes sociales.	Anoche _____ un artículo sobre la salud.
i. Nunca publico nada en Facebook	Hace tres días _____ una foto muy chula

6. Split sentences.

No compro (1)	muchos amigos.
Nunca juego	mi cuenta en Snapchat.
No sigo	nada en línea. (1)
No tengo	por WhatsApp.
No utilizo	descargo vídeos.
Yo chateo	a la PlayStation.
No	mucho tiempo en X.
No me gusta	Facebook.
No paso	a nadie en Instagram.

7. Translate into Spanish.

a. I don't know anybody.

_____

b. I don't buy anything.

_____

c. I don't play anymore.

_____

d. I don't spend much time.

_____

e. No one likes Facebook.

_____

8. Translate into Spanish.

a. I never play online games. _____

b. I spend many hours online every day. _____

c. I don't chat with anyone online. _____

d. I never use social networks. _____

e. There is nothing interesting on TV. _____

f. I never follow anyone on Instagram. _____

g. I have never bought anything online. _____

h. I never download apps. _____

i. I don't watch YouTube videos usually. _____

j. I have never followed any influencers. _____

Preparing for speaking and writing

1. Complete.

a. El or_en_dor [the computer]

b. La he_ _ am_ enta [tool]

c. Tra_uc_r [to translate]

d. Los jó_en_ s [young people]

e. El m_ v_l [the mobile phone]

f. La r_d [the network]

g. Des_ar_ar [to download]

h. La _ant_lla [the screen]

i. Fun_i_nar [to work/function]

j. Las c_m_ras [shopping]

k. En lí_e_ [online]

l. Ju_a_ [to play]

2. Complete with the missing words.

a. Yo uso mi _____ para conectarme a internet.

b. Ayer vi una película de acción _____ Netflix.

c. No me gusta la _____. Es molesta.

d. Yo _____ muchas fotos con mi teléfono.

e. Me encanta _____ con mis compañeros por WhatsApp.

f. Yo comparto _____ por Instagram con frecuencia.

g. ¿_____ (tú) mucho tiempo en las redes sociales?

h. El sábado por la noche vi un _____ de música genial.

i. El fin de semana _____ voy a descansar en casa.

j. Voy a _____ a la PlayStation con mi hermano.

en	hago/saco	publicidad	que viene	chatear
pasas	móvil	programa	fotos	jugar

3. Translate into Spanish.

a. I love: Me e _ _ _ _ _ _

b. My mobile phone: Mi m _ _ _ _

c. A programme: Un p _ _ _ _ _ _ _

d. Social networks: Las r_ _ _ _ sociales

e. In front of the screen: Delante de la p_ _ _ _ _ _ _

f. My favourite website: Mi p_ _ _ _ _ web favorita

g. A digital tool: una herramienta d_ _ _ _ _ _

h. Online: En l_ _ _ _

i. Young people: Los j_ _ _ _ _ _

j. I download: Yo d_ _ _ _ _ _

k. I share: Yo c_ _ _ _ _ _ _

l. I take: Yo t_ _ _

m. Technology: La t_ _ _ _ _ _ _ _ _

n. Online games: Los j_ _ _ _ _ en línea

4. Complete the table.

Infinitive	Present	Preterite Tense	Immediate Future
Ver	Yo veo	Yo vi	Yo voy a ver
Jugar			
Descargar			
Compartir			
Apagar			
Enviar			
Hacer			
Tomar			

5. Tangled translation – translate the words in bold.

a. Yo no compro **nothing** en línea.

b. Ayer yo **broke** mi **mobile phone.**

c. Esta tarde **I am going** a chatear **with** mis amigos **online.**

d. Mi web **favourite** es Teen Vogue**.**

e. Yo no veo **never** series **on** Netflix.

f. Me gusta **to share** fotos **on** Instagram.

g. Yo **watch** a menudo **programmes** de música **on** la tele.

6. Complete with a suitable verb.

a. Yo _____ fotos.

b. Yo _____ la tele.

c. Yo _____ con mis amigos.

d. Yo _____ canciones.

e. Yo _____ con mi ordenador.

f. Yo _____ mensajes de texto.

g. Yo_____ mi ordenador para buscar información.

7. Correct the Spanish translations below.

a. He pasado mucho tiempo en internet.   [I spend a lot of time on the internet]

b. Esta mañana voy a chatear.   [This evening, I am going to chat]

c. Hoy me he comprado un móvil nuevo.   [Today I have bought a new computer]

d. Juego todos los días.   [I play online games every day]

e. Uso mi ordenador para tomar fotos.   [I use my mobile phone to take photos]

f. Voy a descargar algunos vídeos divertidos.   [I have downloaded some fun videos]

g. Hay pocos peligros en internet.   [There are many dangers on the internet]

h. Comparto muchas fotos en Instagram.   [I shared many photos on Instagram]

8. Translate into Spanish.

a. I love my mobile.

_____

b. I use WhatsApp often.

_____

c. My favourite website is…

_____

d. I hate online games.

_____

e. Music apps are good.

_____

f. I do online shopping.

_____

g. I use the internet a lot.

_____

h. I download videos.

_____

i. I share photos.

_____

9. Translate into Spanish.

a. I use my phone to take photos.

b. I share photos and videos.

c. I send messages via *(por)* WhatsApp.

d. My favourite social network is TikTok.

e. I spend lots of time on my phone.

f. I never do my homework on my computer.

g. I use my computer to look for information.

h. I never download music.

i. I use my mobile phone to take photos.

j. I buy things on the internet because it is quick.

k. Teens spend too much time with their mobiles.

l. I prefer podcasts to traditional radio.

m. Last Sunday I downloaded a new music app.

n. Tomorrow I'm going to start a new series on Netflix.

o. This weekend I am going to chat with my friend.

p. I am going to watch a really cool music programme.

Speaking in a role-play

Look at the instructions on the left as they would appear in a speaking test. Read aloud with a partner the dialogue on the right. Then do the dialogue a second time, changing the answers in bold. Take turns playing the two roles.

Foundation (Where you see …, your partner makes up a short reply).

1. Say how you use your phone (give one detail).
2. Say one thing you buy online.
3. Ask your friend a question about social media.
4. Describe a programme you watched on TV recently (give one detail).
5. Say what you think about adverts on TV (give one detail).

1. ¿Qué haces con tu teléfono? **Hago fotos.**
2. ¿Compras algo en línea? **Sí, compro ropa.**
3. ¿Te gustan las redes sociales? …
4. ¿Qué has visto en la tele recientemente? **Un programa de humor.**
5. ¿Cuál es tu opinión sobre la publicidad en la tele? **No me gusta.**

Higher (Where you see …, your partner makes up a short reply).

1. Describe a website you like (give one detail and one opinion).
2. Describe a TV programme you watched recently (give two details).
3. Ask your friend a question about social media.
4. Mention two things you do in your free time.
5. Say what you plan to do next weekend (give two details).

1. ¿Te gusta mucho alguna página web? **Sí, una sobre Fórmula 1. Me encanta.**
2. ¿Qué has visto últimamente en la tele? **He visto un documental sobre animales.**
3. ¿Qué opinas sobre las redes sociales? …
4. ¿Qué haces en tu tiempo libre? **Hago deporte y voy al cine.**
5. ¿Qué vas a hacer el fin de semana que viene? **Voy a un restaurante y voy a jugar al rugby.**

Writing and speaking from a photo card

Describe the photo. Write about who you see, where they are what they are doing. Read out your description.

_____

_____

_____

_____

_____

Answer the following questions related to this topic. Read out your answers.

1. ¿Qué haces con tu móvil?

   _____

   _____

2. ¿Cuál es tu opinión sobre las redes sociales?

   _____

3. ¿Qué redes sociales usas?

   _____

4. ¿Qué páginas web prefieres? ¿Por qué?

   _____

   _____

5. ¿Utilizas las herramientas en línea para hacer tus deberes? ¿Cómo las usas específicamente?

   _____

   _____

6. ¿Qué has hecho recientemente para relajarte?

   _____

   _____

7. ¿Qué piensas de la inteligencia artificial?

   _____

   _____

8. ¿Qué vas a hacer esta tarde después de las clases?

   _____

   _____

Foundation writing

Write about 50 words in Spanish. Write something about each point.

- How you use your phone
- How you use your computer
- Something you don't do with your phone
- A favourite TV show
- A website you like

1. _____
2. _____
3. _____
4. _____
5. _____

Using your knowledge of grammar to complete the sentences below, choosing one of the three options given.

1. Yo _____ los deberes en línea (hago/haces/hacer).

2. A nosotros nos _____ las redes sociales (encantar/encanta/encantan).

3. El fin de semana pasado yo _____ un vídeo en TikTok sobre ese tema (veo/vi/visto).

4. Los vídeos son _____ (entretenidos/entretenidas/entretenido).

5. Yo _____ a dos juegos con mis amigos (juego/juegas/juega).

Foundation/Higher writing

Write approximately 90 words in Spanish. You must refer to each bullet point.

- What you think of social media
- A website you used recently
- A programme you will watch soon

_____
_____
_____
_____
_____
_____
_____

Higher writing

In your exercise book or on paper, write approximately 150 words. You must write something about both bullet points. You can either refer to the language in this unit, for example the sentence bank, or do the task in "exam conditions", without help. Or you could do both!

- The positive and negative aspects of digital technology.
- How you have used your phone **or** a computer recently.

Foundation sentence bank

Tomo fotos con mi móvil.	With my phone I take photos.
Comparto fotos y vídeos.	I share photos and videos.
Envío mensajes por WhatsApp.	I send WhatsApp messages.
Mi red social favorita es TikTok.	My favourite social network is TikTok.
Paso un montón de tiempo con mi móvil.	I spend lots of time on my phone.
Nunca hago los deberes en el ordenador.	I never do my homework on my computer.
Yo creo que las redes sociales son geniales.	I think that social networks are great.
Tienes que tener cuidado en internet.	You have to be careful on the internet.
Subí un vídeo a YouTube.	I posted a video on YouTube.
Ayer tomé algunas fotos de mis amigos.	Yesterday I took some photos of my friends.
Mañana voy a comprar un móvil nuevo.	Tomorrow I am going to buy a new phone.
No me gusta usar el ordenador para jugar.	I do not like to use my computer for games.
Me encanta chatear en línea.	I love to chat online.
Escucho música en Spotify.	I listen to music on Spotify.

Higher sentence bank

El impacto de la tecnología digital es positivo.	The impact of digital technology is positive.
Acabo de comprar un ordenador nuevo.	I've just bought a new computer.
No compro nada en línea a pesar de los bajos precios.	I buy nothing online despite the low prices.
Ya no uso las redes sociales.	I don't use social media anymore.
Lo que me preocupa es el acoso en línea.	What worries me is online bullying.
Los medios digitales han transformado la sociedad.	Digital media have transformed society.
Nadie puede predecir el futuro de la IA.	No one can predict the future of AI.
He aprendido mucho buscando en internet.	I have learned a lot by searching on internet.
Casi nunca descargo música.	I rarely download music.
No compartiré más mis datos personales.	I shall no longer share my personal data.
Te aconsejo no creer todo lo que lees	I advise you not to believe everything that you read.
Al utilizar las redes sociales, estás menos aislado.	By using social media, you are less isolated.
Los adolescentes pasan demasiado tiempo con sus móviles	Teens spend too long on their mobiles.
Prefiero los podcasts a la radio tradicional.	I prefer podcasts to traditional radio.

ANSWERS

Unit 1 Answers
Foundation vocab building

1. Match up.

El corazón	Heart
El cuerpo	Body
Malo	Bad
El pescado	Fish
Bueno	Good
El dolor	Pain
Dieta	Diet
Mejorar	To get better
Deber	To have to
Vapear	To vape
En forma	Fit
Vivir	To live

2. Broken words.

a. Fumar
b. En forma
c. Bueno
d. Beber
e. La leche
f. Cada
g. Intentar
h. Comida
i. Vapear
j. Malo

3. Gapped translation.

a. I am fit.
b. I smoke a lot.
c. I think that...
d. I eat too much.
e. I have a balanced diet.
f. I eat a lot of bread.
g. I don´t like fish.

4. Faulty translation.

a. I eat too much **bread**.
b. Sugar is **good** for your teeth.
c. I **usually** eat fish.
d. I **love** meat.
e. My neck is **so so**.
f. I follow a **balanced** diet.
g. I am **fit**.

5. Anagrams.

a. Dieta
b. Comida
c. Vivir
d. Forma
e. Azúcar
f. Malo
g. Pan
h. Leche

6. Complete the categories...

a. Alimentación (food): carne, pescado, pan.
b. Adjetivos (adjectives): buena, mala, equilibrada
c. Verbos (verbs): comer, intentar, fumar.
d. Bebidas (drinks): leche, agua, zumo de naranja.

7. Translate into English.

a. Sugar
b. Bad
c. Vegetables
d. Fit
e. Good
f. Diet
g. To try
h. Bread
i. Pain

8. Complete the translation.

a. Tengo una **buena** salud.
b. A menudo **como** verduras.
c. Evito **azúcar**.
d. Hago deporte **todos los días**.
e. No bebo **alcohol**.
f. Debes proteger el **corazón**.
g. La comida rápida es **mala** para la salud.
h. Mi madre es muy **activa**.

9. Add the missing letter.

a. **C**uerpo
b. **A**gua
c. **E**vitar
d. **M**alo
e. **B**ueno
f. **E**quilibrado
g. **P**escado
h. **L**eche

10. Multiple choice – circle the right option.

a. Fumar
b. Cuerpo
c. Evitar
d. Comida
e. Mala
f. Alcohol
g. Bueno
h. Intentar
i. Vapear
j. Salud
k. Cada

11. Definitions.

a. Carne
b. Leche
c. Evitar
d. Corazón
e. Mejorar
f. Malo
g. Beber
h. Verduras
i. Vapear
j. Pan

12. Break the flow and translate – mark the gaps and translate.

a. Sigo/una/dieta/equilibrada =   I follow a healthy diet.
b. Como/mucha/verdura =   I eat a lot of vegetables.
c. Hago/deporte/a/menudo =   I often do sports.
d. Normalmente/soy/activa =   I am usually active.
e. Intento/no/fumar/mucho =   I try not to smoke a lot.
f. Nunca/bebo/alcohol =   I never drink alcohol.
g. Estoy/en/forma =   I am fit.
h. Me/gusta/mucho/la/carne =   I like meat very much.
i. A/menudo/como/comida/rápida =   I often eat fast food.

13. Spot and correct the spelling mistakes.

a. Vapear
b. Intentar
c. Alcohol
d. Dieta
e. Malo
f. Pescado
g. Ejercicio
h. Salud
i. Carne

14. Translate into English.
a. I believe that one should have a healthy diet.
b. I eat quite bad becasue I eat too much sugar.
c. I need to eat less sweets.
d. I am fit because I excercise a lot.
e. My grandmother is very active, she goes out often.
f. I don't drink alcohol but I vape a bit.

Foundation reading
1. a) Carlos b) Mercedes c) Sandra d) Andrés e) Marta
2. a) avoids... keeping fit... go out... have fun // b) exercise regularly... front... screen // c) listening... music... reading... cycling
3. a) Half a pitch. b) (i) After 10 minutes (ii) First team to 21 points. c) In the Olympics in 2020. d) Beginners or experienced players.
4. Correct sentences are a, b, e, g, h.
5. a) 3 times a week/for 20 minutes b) Swimming c) Do not sit for too long
6. a) Cycling b) Swimming c) Tired d) Walking

Unit 1 Answers
Higher vocab building

1. Match up.

Dieta	Diet
Poco sano	Not healthy
Hacerse	To become
Azúcar	Sugar
Tiempo	Time
Paseo	A walk
Carne	Meat
Consejo	Advice
Enfermedad	Illness
Bebida	Drink
Dulce	Sweet

2. Broken…
a. Carne
b. Esperar
c. Sin
d. Azúcar
e. Nadar
f. Dormir
g. Tiempo
h. Bebida
i. Sentirse
j. Consejo

3. Gapped translation.
a. To go **walking.**
b. To keep **fit.**
c. Eat a **healthy** lunch.
d. To avoid **fatty foods.**
e. A **sweet** drink.
f. To be **vegan.**
g. A coffee **without** sugar.
h. To **reduce** stress.

4. Faulty translation.
a. A **balanced diet** is necessary.
b. I drank a **sweet** drink.
c. **I try** to **lose** weight.
d. He is very **ill.**
e. What do you **advise** me?
f. **I became** vegetarian.

5. Definitions.
a. Dulce
b. Alimentación
c. Vegetariano/a, Vegano/a
d. Descansar
e. Sano
f. Dormir
g. Se debe
h. Tomar
i. Sin

6. Complete the categories…
a. Descansar, sentir, dormir, reducir
b. Enfermo, sano, dulce
c. Alimentación, enfermedad, tiempo, éxito
d. Recientemente

7. Translate into English.
a. Advice
b. To walk
c. Time
d. To reduce
e. Sugar
f. To become
g. To hope
h. To rest
i. To swim

8. Complete.
a. Dieta
b. Hago
c. Pasear
d. Vegetariano
e. Activa
f. Evito
g. Tiempo
h. Nadar
i. Gustaría

9. Add in…
a. Un paseo largo
b. Poco sano
c. Bebida
d. Tiempo
e. Consejo
f. **C**onvertirse
g. **V**egano
h. Dulc**e**

10. MC.
a. Advice
b. To sleep
c. To eat
d. To hope
e. Ill
f. Sugar
g. Meat
h. Time
i. To feel
j. To swim

11. Defs.
a. Azúcar
b. Consejo
c. Dormir
d. Natación
e. Esperar
f. Últimamente
g. Alimentación
h. Vegetariano
i. Malsano/Enfermo

12. Translate into English.
a. Last weekend I was ill.
b. I have changed my diet.
c. It is necessary to/One has to consume less sugar.
d. I try to avoid sweet drinks.
e. I started to go swimming two times a week.
f. I often do long walks in the countryside.

13. Transpuzzle.
a. El número de gente obesa aumenta (The number of obese people increases).
b. Decidí cambiar mi dieta (I decided to change my diet).
c. Hay que comer alimentos más sanos (One has to eat healthier food).
d. Espero no ponerme enfermo (I hope I don't get sick)
e. Empecé a hacer largas caminatas en la montaña (I started taking long hikes in the mountains).
f. No pongo azúcar en mi café (I don't put sugar in my coffee).
g. Me gustaría hacer más ejercicio (I would like to exercise more).
h. Una buena alimentación previene las enfermedades (A good diet prevents diseases).
i. Mi médico me ha aconsejado hacerme vegano (My doctor has advised me to become a vegan).

Higher reading

1. 1) Eat a balance diet = lots of fruit, veg and protein. 2) Drink water throughout the day. 3) 30 minutes exercise a day. 4) Sleep 7-9 hours a night. 5) Avoid sugar. 6) Do not smoke or drink much alcohol. 7) Reduce stress by relaxation exercises. 8) Spend time outside. 9) See a doctor regularly. 10) Have a positive attitude.

2. each/every… healthy… home-made… playing football… after school… stay active… lots of water… hot months… rice… lots of vegetables.

3. 1) a. improve health, b. help with daily life.   2) 150 minutes per week.   3) Muscle-based work/weights at least twice a week. 4) Meeting new people.   5) Using a wheelchair can make exercises harder.   6) Team sports.

4. 1) Take short breaks. 2) Breathe deeply. 3) Do exercise.   4) Listen to quiet/calm music. 5) Make a list of activities – decide which are important (Get organised).   6) Talk to someone.

5. 1) Stomachaches at night.   2) Change his way of eating/diet.   3) Vegetables, fruit, rice.   4) Feels better, feels with energy.

Grammar focus – Part 1 – The Preterite Tense
Preterite tense of REGULAR -AR Verbs

1. Match up.

Mejorar	To improve
Terminar	To finish
Ganar	To win
Necesitar	To need
Ayudar	To help
Apoyar	To support
Comprar	To buy
Entrenar	To train
Fumar	To smoke
Engordar	To put on weight
Adelgazar	To lose weight
Descansar	To rest

2. Complete.

a. Yo **compré** verduras esta mañana.

b. La condición física de Juan no **mejoró** porque no **entrenó.**

c. Ellos **fumaron** mucho.

d. Nosotros **ayudamos** a Juan con la rutina de ejercicios.

e. Yo **entrené** con mi padre.

f. Vosotros **ganasteis** el torneo de fútbol.

3. Circle with the correct form.

a. Compré

b. Ganamos

c. Prepararon

d. Descansaste

e. Fumó

f. Apoyé

g. Terminaron

Preterite tense of REGULAR -ER/IR verbs

1. Circle the correct preterite tense form.

a. Comí

b. Perdimos

c. Comieron

d. Dormiste

e. Bebió

f. Aprendí

g. Decidieron

2. Complete with the correct...

a. Comí

b. Vivió

c. Corrieron

d. Decidimos

e. Escribí

3. Complete the table.

Infinitive	Preterite Tense
Comprar	Yo compré
Entrenar	**Yo entrené**
Engordar	Yo engordé
Comer	Yo comí
Beber	**Yo bebí**
Perder	**Yo perdí**
Escribir	Yo escribí
Vivir	**Yo viví**
Decidir	Yo decidí

4. Add the missing letters.

a. Compr**ó**

b. Se levant**ó**

c. Viv**imos**

d. Beb**ieron**

e. Comi**ó**

f. Escrib**í**

g. Engord**ó**

h. Perd**í**

5. Translate into English.

a. I lost 10 kilos.

b. You trained at the gym.

c. You (formal) ate very healthy.

d. I lived in the countryside.

e. Did you play football yesterday?

f. You (plural) put on weight.

g. They drank water.

h. What did you (formal, plural) ate?

i. My mother bought fish.

j. I didn't drink coffee.

Preterite tense of KEY IRREGULAR verbs

1. Circle the correct...

a. Ellos

b. Yo

c. Nosotros

d. Tú

e. Nosotros

f. Vosotros

g. Ella

h. Nosotros

2. Correct the...

a. Hizo

b. Fuimos

c. Tuvo

d. Fue

e. Hicieron

f. Fuiste

g. Tuvieron

h. Tuve

3. Insert the correct...

a. Hice

b. Fuiste

c. Hizo

d. Hicimos

e. Tuve

f. Fue

4. Complete the sentences below.

a. Fui

b. Fuisteis

c. Hizo

d. Fueron

e. Hicieron

f. Tuve

g. Tuvo

5. Complete with the missing letters.

a. Compr**é**   d. H**izo**

b. F**uimos**   e. F**uisteis**

c. Engord**aron**   f. Beb**ieron**

6. Translate into Spanish.

a. Tú perdiste peso.   d. Yo fui a clase de yoga.

b. Ellas fueron al gimnasio. e. Ellos hicieron deporte.

c. Nosotros comimos pasta.   f. Ella hizo boxeo.

Useful verbs with a FIRST PERSON spell change + REFLEXIVE verbs

1. Match up.

Yo jugué	I played
Yo fui	I went
Yo busqué	I looked for
Yo hice	I did
Yo entrené	I trained
Yo practiqué	I practised
Yo engordé	I put on weight
Yo pagué	I paid
Yo tuve	I had
Yo adelgacé	I lost weight

2. Translate into English.

a. I did
b. I ate
c. I looked for
d. I practised
e. I bought
f. I drank
g. I swam
h. I had
i. I lost weight
j. I played
k. I went
l. I lost
m. I trained
n. I skied

3. Complete the words.

a. Me acosté
b. Se levantó
c. Te encontraste
d. Se pesó
e. Nos levantamos
f. Me lavé
g. Te acostaste

4. Correct the translation errors.

a. **They (F)** weighed themselves.
b. **They (M)** went to bed.
c. **You (formal)** relaxed.
d. **We** relaxed.
e. **You (formal)** went to bed.
f. **You (singular)** weighed **yourself**.
g. **You (plural)** went to bed.

Grammar focus – Part 2 – The Perfect Tense

Perfect tense of REGULAR -AR verbs

1. Circle the correct...

a. Nosotros
b. Ella
c. Ellos
d. Usted
e. Yo
f. Vosotros
g. Tú
h. Ella
i. Ellos
j. Yo
k. Tú

2. Translate.

a. Yo he bailado.
b. Nosotros hemos escuchado.
c. Tú has nadado.
d. Mi madre ha jugado al tenis.
e. Mis padres han comprado un coche.
f. Él ha tomado un café.
g. Nosotros hemos comprado agua.
h. Ellos han estudiado durante dos horas.
i. ¿Han jugado ellos antes?
j. Yo he estudiado para el examen.
k. Ella ha bailado con su amigo/a.

Perfect tense of REGULAR -ER/IR verbs

1. Match up.

He comido	I have eaten
He bebido	I have drunk
He salido	I have gone out
He subido	I have uploaded
He dormido	I have slept
He vivido	I have lived
He seguido	I have followed
He podido	I have been able to
He ido	I have gone
He tenido	I have had
He sido	I have been

2. Translate into English.

a. I have gone out.
b. You (singular) have gone.
c. We have lived.
d. You (plural) have drunk.
e. I have slept.
f. She has followed.
g. We have been able to.
h. I have eaten.
i. I have been.
j. You (singular) have been able to.
k. They have gone out.
l. I have lived.
m. You (singular) have slept.
n. They have had.

3. Correct the mistakes in the words....

a. **Ha** ido
b. **Hemos** ido
c. **He** tenido
d. **Ha** ido
e. **Han** salido
f. **Has** ido
g. **Habéis/han** tenido
h. **Has** dormido

4. Correct the translation errors.

a. **They (F)** have eaten.
b. They have **not** been able to go.
c. **You (formal)** have gone out.
d. **We** have slept.
e. **He** has had a problem.
f. **You (singular)** have followed a new health influencer.
g. **You (plural)** have gone to the cinema.
h. Today **I** have eaten well.

5. Translate into Spanish.

a. Yo he escuchado.
b. Nosotros hemos salido.
c. Ellos han comido.
d. Tú has ido a la playa.
e. Vosotros habéis bebido agua.
f. Yo he seguido a un nuevo influencer.
g. He tenido un problema.
h. Ellos han nadado en la piscina.
i. Nosotros hemos bailado en la discoteca.
j. Yo he dormido toda la noche.

Perfect tense of key verbs with IRREGULAR participles

1. Insert the correct conjugated verb.

a. Yo he **hecho** un curso de natación.
b. ¿Usted ha **abierto** la puerta?
c. Tú has **visto** la película nueva de...
d. Nosostros hemos **escrito** una carta.
e. Yo he **vuelto** a casa hace tres horas.
f. Ella ha **roto** su móvil.

2. Complete the sentences below with a logical verb (accept other correct answers).

a. Escrito
b. Visto
c. Hecho
d. Vuelto
e. Hecho
f. Descubierto
g. Roto

3. Complete with the missing letters.

a. Yo he **roto** mi móvil (I have broken my phone).
b. Nosotros hemos **hecho** (we have done).
c. Ellos han **vuelto** (they have returned).
d. Ella ha **escrito** (she has written).
e. Vosotros habéis **visto** (you, plural, have seen).
f. Ustedes han **abierto** (you have opened).
g. Mi hámster ha **muerto** (my hamster has died).
h. ¿Tú has **dicho** hola? (have you said hello?).

4. Translate into Spanish.

a. I have done a course - He **hecho** un **curso.**
b. You have returned from the gym - Has **vuelto** del. **gimnasio.**
c. We have done many things- H**emos** **hecho** m**uchas** c**osas.**
d. Today I saw my friend- H**oy** he **visto** a mi a**migo.**
e. They have said hello- H**an** **dicho** h**ola.**

5. Translate into Spanish.

a. He roto mi móvil.
b. Has vuelto del colegio/de la escuela.
c. (Él) Ha hecho muchas cosas hoy.
d. He escrito una carta a mi amigo.

e. (Ella) Ha dicho hola.
f. Mi hermano ha descubierto un juego nuevo.
g. (Ellos/Ellas) Han abierto la puerta.
h. Esta mañana he visto a mi amigo/a.

Unit 1 Answers
Preparing for speaking and writing

1. Complete the table.

Español	Inglés
Vapear	**To vape**
Verduras	Vegetables
No es saludable	**It's unhealthy**
Vegetariano	Vegetarian
El senderismo	**Hiking**
Una buena salud	Good health
Mi plato favorito	**My favourite dish**
Una dieta sana	A healthy diet
Una buena comida	**A good meal**
Últimamente	Recently
Es malo	**It's bad**
Duermo	I sleep
Yo evito	**I avoid**

2. Gapped translation.

a. Como
b. Libre
c. Sigo
d. Es
e. Mañana
f. Vapeo
g. Hago
h. Prefiero
i. Creo
j. Estoy

3. Sentence puzzle.

a. A menudo yo como sano.

b. Para estar en forma sigo una dieta equilibrada.

c. El estrés es malo para la salud.

d. Vapear es muy malo para la salud.

e. Yo duermo al menos ocho horas cada noche.

4. Complete the words with missing letters.

a. Yo vap**eo**   i. Yo e**vito**
b. M**a**lo   j. Co**razón**
c. Die**ta**   k. Yo d**uermo**
d. Sa**lud**   l. A m**enudo**
e. S**ano**   m. Yo **pienso**
f. Yo co**mo**   n. Equili**brado**
g. La com**ida** o. Ver**duras**
h. No **sano**   p. Yo me q**uedo**

5. Complete the table.

Infinitive	Present
Comer	Yo como
Beber	Yo bebo
Tomar	Yo tomo
Evitar	Yo evito
Hacer	Yo hago
Ser	Yo soy
Tener	Yo tengo

6. Complete the translation.

a. Para **estar** en forma **hago** ejercicio.

b. En mi **colegio** podemos hacer **natación.**

c. La próxima **semana** voy a montar en bicicleta.

d. Para **estar** más sano voy a hacerme **vegano.**

e. **Vapear** es malo para la **salud.**

f. Recientemente he **comido** más **verduras.**

g. Para **mejorar** mi **forma** hago más deporte.

7. Translate into Spanish

a. **Me gusta c**omer pollo.
b. **Me gusta b**eber Coca-Cola.
c. **V**oy al **gimnasio.**
d. **Es s**ano.
e. Va**pear** no es **s**ano.
f. **Yo estoy** en **f**orma.
g. **V**oy a **nadar.**
h. **H**ago de**porte.**
i. **D**uermo **o**cho **h**oras.

8. From present to past.

Present	Perfect Tense
Yo vapeo	Yo he vapeado
Yo juego	Yo he jugado
Yo como	Yo he comido
Yo tomo	Yo he tomado
Yo hago	Yo he hecho
Yo nado	Yo he nadado
Yo duermo	Yo he dormido
Yo me levanto	Yo me he levantado

9. Complete...

a. Estar
b. Voy
c. Debo/intento
d. Comido
e. Duermo
f. Voy a
g. Fui
h. Tomado
i. Juego/salgo
j. Tengo
k. Estoy
l. Hago
m. Acuesto

10. Translate into Spanish.

a. Me gusta ir en bicicleta y jugar al fútbol con mis amigos.

b. Es importante seguir una dieta equilibrada.

c. En general, el estrés es malo para la salud.

d. Tienes que/debes intentar hacer ejercicio cada día/todos los días.

e. Pienso que tengo una dieta sana.

f. Me mantengo sano evitando el alcohol y las drogas.

g. El domingo que viene voy a hacer senderismo en el campo.

h. Cuando era más joven solía comer demasiado azúcar.

i. Si tuviera más tiempo jugaría al fútbol cada tarde/todas las tardes.

j. He estado en la piscina con mis amigos.

k. Antes de comer hice un poco de ejercicio.

Unit 2 Answers

Foundation vocab building

1. Match up.

Dinero	Money
Programa	Programme
Cantante	Singer
Éxito	Success
Entrevista	Interview
Escritor	Writer
Boda	Wedding
Llevar	To wear
Carrera	Career
Cantar	To sing

2. Complete.

a. Famosa
b. Escritor
c. Influencer
d. Rico
e. Boda
f. Actor
g. Actriz
h. Moda
i. Programa
j. Cantante

3. Unjumble...

a. Periódico – Newspaper
b. Escuchar – To listen
c. Seguir – To follow
d. Modelo – Model
e. Escritor – Writer
f. Carrera – Career
g. Actriz – Actress
h. Vídeo – Video
i. Equipo – Team
j. Llevar - To wear
k. Autor – Author
l. Telerrealidad - Reality TV

4. Fix any incorrect English translations.

a. Periódico: **Newspaper**
b. Cantante: Singer
c. Carrera: **Career**
d. Seguir: **To follow**
e. Escritora: Writer
f. Llevar: **To wear**
g. Equipo: **Team**
h. Dinero: Money
i. Escuchar: **To listen**
j. Programa: **Programme**
k. Entrevista: Interview
l. Cantar: **To sing**

5. Complete the trans...

a. Famous
b. Influencer
c. Good
d. Think (that)
e. Character
f. Politician
g. Songs
h. Singer

6. Sentence puzzle.

a. Es mi actriz favorita porque es única.
b. Me encantan sus canciones y su estilo.
c. Es un actor muy bueno y me encantan sus películas.
d. Es famoso por su papel en la película Thor.
e. Fui a su concierto la semana pasada.
f. Es una modelo muy famosa y rica.
g. Me gusta porque es famoso pero humilde.
h. Es una estrella del cine.

7. Circle the correct translation.

a.		interview	
b.			fashion
c.			team
d.	good		
e.	to follow		
f.		money	
g.			famous
h.		singer	
i.		to wear	
j.		actor	
k.		with him	

8. Complete with the correct option.

a. Él **juega** para el equipo de Real Madrid.
b. Ella es famosa por sus **películas** de acción.
c. Ella canta una bonita **canción**.
d. Él es muy famoso y **rico**.
e. Es un actor y un **cantante** excelente.
f. Juega un **papel** de superhéroe.
g. He **visto** todas sus películas.
h. Ayer vi una entrevista con él en la **tele**.

9. Translate into English.

a. He is a very popular footballer.
b. She is an excellent actress and singer.
c. I saw an interview with him. It was great!
d. I like his look and character a lot.
e. She is famous for her romantic comedies.
f. I went to two of his/her concerts.
g. I follow Taylor Swift on Instagram.
h. I don't follow any influencers on social media.
i. He is known for a role in Star Wars.
j. She is a rich and famous model.
k. He has had a long career in sport.
l. My brothers follow a lot of influencers.
m. My favourite writer is J.K. Rowling.

Foundation reading

1. a) Emilio   b) Clara   c) Clara   d) Emilo   e) Abel   f) Abel

2. a) Long   b) Sunday   c) Singer

3. a) Miriam   b) Sara   c) Javier   d) Javier   e) Sara   f) Manu

4. a) Because it is interesting   b) Interested in fashion (likes fashion)   c) Mental health issues   d) Social issues/poverty

5. Lisa P   Mateo N   Valentina N   Alejandro P   Aitana P/N

6. a) Singer... voice... first   b) Identify   c) Spends a lot ... second

Unit 2 Answers
Higher vocab building

1. Compare the English words below with their Spanish equivalent.

Español	English	Español	English
Anunciar	Announce	Víctima	Victim
Elegante	Elegant	Heroína	Heroin
Premio	Prize	Inspirado	Inspired
Héroe	Hero	Famoso	Famous
Publicar	To publish	Teatro	Theatre
Novela	Novel	Publicidad	Publicity
Escándalo	Scandal	Presentar	To present
Voz	Voice	Persona	Person

2. Match up .

Red	Network
Periódico	Newspaper
Novela	Novel
Seguir	To follow
Orgulloso/a	Proud
Publicar	To publish
Marca	Brand
Voz	Voice

3. Complete/translate.

a. Publicar: to publish

b. Poderoso: powerful

c. Redes: networks

d. Seguir: to follow

e. Gira: tour

f. Premio: prize

g. Marca: brand

4. Translate into English.

a. Rosalía has a great voice.

b. Pablo Alborán visits many cities during his tours.

c. He/she was an attack victim.

d.The lyrics of his songs are very beautiful.

5. Sentence puzzle.

a. Me encanta su voz porque es muy potente.

b. La sigo en las redes sociales.

c. Ella está de gira en Europa.

d. Me inspiran él y su personaje.

6. Anagrams.

a. Voz   f. Reconocer

b. Gira   g. Papel

c. Presentar   h. Admirar

d. Orgulloso   i. Ropa

e. Anuncio   j. Marca

7. Complete.

a. Potente.

b. Redes.

c. Gira.

d. Concierto.

e. Lleva.

f. Inspira.

g. Películas.

h. Buenas.

8. Fix the translations.

a. Admirar: to admire.

b. Quedar: to meet.

c. Orgulloso: proud.

d. La heroína: heroin.

e. El periódico: the newspaper.

f. La marca: brand.

g. La apertura: opening.

h. La letra: lyrics.

i. El anuncio: advertising.

9. Translate into English.

a. A star of fashion.

b. A very proud woman.

c. A new brand.

d. (Some) interesting lyrics.

e. (Some) funny adverts.

f. An important role.

g. He has published a new novel.

h. The theatre opening.

i. To win an important prize.

10. Translate into English.

a. He is my favourite author. He writes very good novels.

b. She is my favourite singer. She has a powerful voice and I love the lyrics of her songs.

c. I admire her because she has a lot of talent, plus she has a beautiful voice.

d. What I like most, is that, even though she is rich and famous, she is very modest.

e. I don't follow influencers like him online because they talk a lot of nonsense.

f. After seeing his last series, I followed him on Instagram.

Higher reading

1. Correct statements are a, c and e.

2. a) A gold medal at the London Olympics.   b) One gold and one bronze medal.   c) Award-winning.

   d) He was another flag bearer with Mireia   e) She loves fashion, has a dog called London and studies Advertising/Public Relations.

3. a) Six months before the concert.   b) A garden.   c) Unforgettable.   d) The lyrics.   e) She talks about mental health.

4. 1c   2a   3c   4b

5. a) TikTok and Instagram.   b) Traveling.   c) She went to Argentina.   d) She has a young daughter + her partner is called Adrián.

   e) A festival for mothers who travel

6. 1c   2b   3a   4b

Unit 2 Answers
Grammar focus - Talking or writing about the future

a. FUT	Tomorrow I'm going to the cinema in town.
b. PRES	Every day I watch Instagram.
c. PRES	I listen to my favourite singer.
d. FUT	Next weekend I'm going to a concert.
e. FUT	I'm going to see my favourite actress at the cinema.
f. FUT	I shall watch my favourite series.
g. FUT	I'm going to go to the concert; it will be great!
h. PAST	I went to see a show at the theatre.
i. PRES	I upload videos on Snapchat almost every day.
j. FUT	My mother is going to listen to her favourite album.
j. PAST	We saw a famous person.
k. FUT	Tomorrow we are going to watch Netflix.
l. PAST	I saw the new James Bond movie.
m. PRES	I follow my favourite actor on X.

1. Match up.

Seguir	To follow
Anunciar	To announce
Ir	To go
Llevar	To wear
Salir	To go out
Ganar	To win
Comprar	To buy
Mirar	To watch
Ver	To see
Leer	To read
Publicar	To publish
Subir	To upload
Escuchar	To listen

2. Ir.

a. Va

b. Van

c. Vamos

d. Voy

e. Va

f. Vamos

g. Van

h. Vas

i. Va

j. Vais

3. Missing letters.

a. Yo **voy** a comp**r**ar.

b. Nosotros **vamos** a cam**b**iar.

c. Ellos **van a** seg**uir.**

d. Ella **va** a sa**lir.**

e. Vosotros **vais** a **v**er.

4. Translate.

a. Vamos a cambiar nuestro coche hoy.

b. Él va a ganar un premio por su última película.

c. Voy a seguir a Ariana Grande en Instagram.

d. Ella va a publicar sus fotos en las redes sociales.

e. Ellas van a ir a su concierto mañana.

f. Él va a anunciar su boda esta noche.

g. ¿Vas a ver su programa hoy?

h. Esta tarde voy a escuchar sus canciones.

5. Verb endings.

a. Yo veré.

b. Ella irá.

c. Nosotros le esperaremos.

d. Publicarán.

e. Usted publicará.

f. Vosotros seguiréis.

6. Complete with the correct ending.

a. Ella ver**á**.

b. Nosotros ser**emos.**

c. Yo escuchar**é**.

d. Usted anunciar**á**.

e. Ellos har**án.**

f. Tú comprar**ás.**

g. Vosotros ir**éis.**

h. Él ir**á**.

i. Ellos ganar**án.**

j. Vosotros estar**éis.**

k. Tú leer**ás.**

l. Yo anunciar**é**.

7. Complete the table.

Infinitivo	Presente	Futuro simple
Hacer	Hago	Haré
Publicar	Publico	Publicaré
Salir	Salgo	Saldré
Escuchar	Escucho	Escucharé
Comprar	Compro	Compraré
Ser	Soy	Seré
Tener	Tengo	Tendré
Asistir	Asisto	Asistiré
Mirar	Miro	Miraré
Ver	Veo	Veré

8. Complete.

a. Esperaré

b. Seguiremos

c. Anunciarán

d. Verás

e. Escucharán

f. Compraremos

g. Ganará

h. Compraré

9. Translate into Spanish.

a. Esperaré a su nuevo álbum.

b. Él ganará un premio.

c. Vamos a comprarle un perfume nuevo.

d. Ella será más famosa.

e. El año que viene ella publicará una novela nueva.

f. Anunciarán su matrimonio pronto.

g. Escucharé su nueva canción.

h. La esperaremos en la entrada al estadio.

i. Ella será famosa muy pronto.

j. Esta tarde van a ver su última serie.

k. La seguiré en las redes sociales.

l. La semana que viene iremos a su concierto en Valencia.

Unit 2 Answers
Preparing for speaking and writing

1. Complete.

Spanish
La moda
El programa
Yo vi
El pasatiempo
El famoso
Recientemente
Favorito
Ventaja
Famoso
Letra

2. Complete.

a. Favorita

b. Llama

c. Cantante

d. Creo

e. Redes

f. Voy

g. Pasatiempo

h. Canciones

3. Gapped translation.

a. que viene…ir

b. Mi…favorita

c. alta…guapa

d. veré…cine

e. cantante…nueva

f. programas…moda

g. Mañana…ver

4. Complete.

a. Moda

b. Premio

c. Gira

d. Marca

e. Actor

f. Famoso

g. Orgulloso

h. Canción

i. Preferir

j. Papel

k. Actriz

l. Las noticias

m. Programa

n. Ver

o. Cantante

p. Gustar

q. Comedia

r. Escritor

5. Add the missing accents.

a. Mi película favorita es "Lo imposible".

b. Hoy no hay programas sobre fútbol en la tele.

c. Odio las novelas de ciencia ficción.

d. Hemos subido un vídeo a Snapchat.

e. Ella no será famosa en el futuro.

f. Él no tiene vida privada.

g. Yo veo series de televisión.

h. Yo prefiero su última canción.

i. Luego subiré unas fotos a Instagram.

6. Tenses.

a. Es

b. Es

c. Voy

d. Vamos a ver

e. Seré

f. Gusta

g. Voy a ver

h. Escuchar

7. Translate.

a. Graciosa

b. Alto

c. Delgado

d. Guapa

e. Orgullosa

f. Tonto

g. Famosa

h. Rico

i. Buena

8. Translate into Spanish (easier).

a. Él es rico.

b. Ella es famosa.

c. Lo respeto.

d. La admiro.

e. Escucho sus canciones.

f. Me gusta la letra.

g. Me inspira.

h. Ella es muy orgullosa.

i. Veo sus películas.

j. Él es un superhéroe.

k. Me encanta la moda.

l. Ella es una estrella.

m. Él es rico y famoso.

n. Él juega al futbol.

o. Ella tiene una buena voz.

p. Me encanta su ropa.

9. Translate into Spanish (harder).

a. La admiro por su talento.

b. Lo que más me gusta es su poderosa voz.

c. Es la mejor novela que he leído.

d. Acabo de ir a un concierto de mi grupo favorito.

e. Después de ver la película, lo seguí en Instagram.

f. La letra de las canciones es lo que más me gusta.

g. El lunes que viene voy a verla.

h. En mi opinión es una actriz fabulosa.

i. Él ha publicado muchas novelas que me gustan.

j. Hace dos años la vi en un escenario en Londres.

k. Muchos jóvenes siguen a los famosos.

l. Vamos a salir. ¡Será genial!

m. Voy a ver mi programa favorito en YouTube.

n. Me inspira su poderosa voz.

Unit 3 Answers

Foundation vocab building

1. Match up.

Ruido	Noise
Sol	Sun
Reciclar	Recycling
Agua	Water
Frío	Cold
Basura	Waste
Calor	Hot
Hambre	Hunger
Fábricas	Factories
Granja	Farm
Costa	Coast

2. Correct the wrong translations.

a. Guapo: **handsome**

b. En verano: in the **summer**

c. El cielo es azul: the **sky** is blue

d. Mucho ruido: a lot of **noise**

e. Hace frío: it is **cold**

f. En la costa: **on the coast**

g. El bosque: The **forest**

h. El calentamiento: **warming**

3. One of three – circle the right answer.

Sol		sun	
Basura	waste		
Falta	lack		
Mundo		world	
Tirar			to throw
Ruido			noise
Tierra		Earth	
Fábrica	factory		
Vivir			to live
Lugar		place	

4. Negatives.

a. Destruir ✔

b. Amenazar ✔

c. Construir

d. Cabricar

e. Contaminar ✔

f. Mejorar

g. Vivir

h. Matar ✔

i. Reciclar

5. Complete.

a. Warming

b. Sunny

c. Waste / rubbish

d. Water

e. Sea

f. Rubbish bins

6. Translate.

a. Factory

b. Wind

c. To live

d. The lack of

e. Danger

f. World

g. Light

h. Beach

i. Sea

j. Own

k. Winter

l. Threat

7. Sentence puzzle.

a. En mi pueblo hay mucha contaminación.

b. Es necesario reducir la cantidad de basura.

c. No hay suficientes cubos de basura en las calles.

d. Las temperaturas están aumentando cada verano.

e. Lo que me preocupa es la destrucción de los bosques.

f. Yo vivo en un pueblo bonito en el sur del país.

g. La falta de recursos naturales es preocupante.

8. Translate into English.

a. Waste recycling.

b. Air pollution.

c. What worries me.

d. The lack of water.

e. Toxic waste.

f. Huge waste.

g. Polluting vehicles.

h. We recycle paper.

i. Water pollution.

j. It is always good weather.

k. The serious threat.

l. I turn off the lights.

m. I throw away rubbish.

n. You clean the bin.

o. The factories pollute.

p. A clean bicycle.

9. Translate into English.

a. Water pollution is the main problem in my region.

b. What worries me the most is air pollution.

c. There are always many polluting vehicles driving on the roads.

d. It shocks me to see the amount of litter and other waste that people throw on the street.

e. Electric cars are very expensive, but they are good for the environment.

f. I think that it is very important to protect the environment.

g. I buy as few clothes as possible and I give my old clothes to charities.

h. I always use public transport to pollute the atmosphere less.

i. I recycle plastics, metal cans and paper.

j. I think that the climate change is the number one problem in the world.

k. In my opinion, people do not worry enough about the environment.

l. I'm going to make a bigger effort in the future, I think.

m. I am not optimistic about the future of the planet.

Foundation reading

1. a) Samuel   b) Carlos   c) Laura   d) Carlos   e) Laura   f) Samuel
2. a) Countryside   b) Trees   c) Car
3. Indiana P   Mohamed N   Paloma P/N   Marcos P
4. 1b   2a   3c
5. a) Climate crisis/change.   b) They don't make a big enough effort.   c) Young people going on strike.   d) Nor optimistic (pessimistic).
6. Problem: Water   Solution: reduce industrial pollution
   Problem: Dirty energy   Solution: Use clean energy
   Problem: Forests shrinking   Solution: Protect the forests
7. a) Climate warming
   b) Heat waves and less rain
   c) There is less rainfall
   d) They will melt and disappear

Unit 3 Answers

Higher vocab building

1. Match up.

Amenaza	Threat
Encender	To turn on
Afueras	Suburbs
Guerra	War
Madera	Wood
Vidrio	Glass
Sucio	Dirty
Hambre	Hunger
Necesidad	Need
Limpio	Clean
Seguro	Safe

2. Wrong translations.

a. Gestionar: to manage

b. Caja: **box**

c. Hambre: hunger

d. Intenso: **intense**

e. Quemar: to **burn**

f. Lugar: **place**

g. Preocupado: **worried**

h. Dar: to **give**

3. One of three – right answers

		threat	
to give			
			scenery
		to fight	
tax			
		dirty	
safe			
		glass	
		clean	
war			
			factory

4. Tick adjectives.

a. **Preocupado**: worried

b. Caja

c. **Guapo**: handsome

d. **Sucio**: dirty

e. **Limpio**: clean

f. Afueras

g. Muerte

h. Lluvia

i. **Seguro**: safe

j. **Solar**: solar

5. Complete the translations.

a. The pollution of **rivers.**

b. Acid **rain.**

c. A **clean** town.

d. A **safe** neighbourhood.

e. To increase **taxes.**

f. The **suffering** of animals.

6. Translate.

a. Clean

b. To save

c. To fight

d. Threat

e. Tax

f. Worried

g. Landscape

h. To destroy

i. Dirty

j. Solar

k. Factory

l. War

7. Sentence puzzle.

a. Debemos evitar usar bolsas de plástico.

b. Hay que reducir las emisiones de gas carbono.

c. Es necesario limitar el consumo del agua.

d. Debemos salvar las especies en peligro de extinción.

e. Es importante reciclar la basura.

f. Quiero vivir en un barrio limpio y seguro.

g. El paisaje alrededor de mi pueblo es muy bonito.

8. Translate into English:

a. (The) plastic bags.

b. We/you must recycle.

c. A dirty neighbourhood.

d. River pollution.

e. The worst thing is noise.

f. (The) polluting vehicles.

g. To increase taxes.

h. The threat of extinction.

i. To plant trees.

j. To turn on lights.

k. To recycle wood.

l. The need for energy.

m. A beautiful landscape.

n. It's worrying.

o. Life in the countryside.

p. (The) factories pollute.

9. Translate into English.

a. Wind turbines are clean and cheaper.

b. I have just read an article about the climate crisis

c. In the future the level of the oceans will rise.

d. Renewable energy sources will be vital.

e. We'll have to fight to protect the environment.

f. Poor populations suffer the most.

g. Rare species are in danger of extinction.

h. In my opinion, it's the most important subject.

i. Nuclear energy is going to play an important role

j. I have decided to buy fewer new clothes.

k. My mother will no longer travel by plane.

l. Climate change worries me.

m. Governments will have to do more.

Higher reading

1. a) Two of: cleaned neighbourhood/local area – picked up rubbish/waste – planted trees.
   b) Learned importance of working together and caring for/looking after the planet.
   c) Creating stronger relationships with neighbours.
   d) Tw of: good for nature – good for themselves – good for future generations.
2. Correct statements are b and c.
3. a) P   b) N   c) F   d) P
4. a) Three of: rising sea levels – climate change – coanimal habitat destruction – number of tourists.
   b) They are seeking solutions.
   c) Protecting coasts – promoting eco-friendly tourism – protecting animal species.
   d) Protecting natural life.
5. a) Greenly   b) Blablacar   c) Breezo Meter   d) Too Good to Go   e) GoGreen Challenge
6. a) Creates clothes out of recycled materials – they clean the seas.
   b) In 2009 Javier Goyenche decided to start making clothes form recycled materials.
   c) Over 1800 shops in 40 countries, 150 employees.

Unit 3 Answers
Grammar focus - The Conditional Tense

a. FUT	I will recycle more paper.
b. FUT	He will recycle more plastic(s).
c. PRES	I always turn off the lights.
d. COND	I would use public transport.
e. FUT	You will travel less often by plane.
f. PRES	My family recycles lots of waste.
g. FUT	We will drive by electric car.
h. COND	We would drive by hybrid car.
i. PRES	We often take the train.
j. COND	I could/might reduce my carbon footprint.
k. COND	I should/ought to consume less meat.
l. COND	I could eat organic produce.
m. COND	I would like to waste less energy.
n. PRES	We recycle paper and glass.
o. PRES	I often use my bicycle.
p. FUT	I will buy organic produce.
q. COND	I would buy fewer new clothes.

1. Match up.

Destruir	To destroy
Tirar	To throw (away)
Actuar	To act
Limpiar	To clean
Contaminar	To pollute
Mejorar	To improve
Viajar	To travel
Utilizar	To use
Aumentar	To increase
Reducir	To reduce

2. Complete the table.

Conditional
Reciclaría
Viviríamos
Limpiarían
Comprarías
Mejorarían
Tendríamos
Podríais
Querría
Deberían
Venderías

3. Choose the correct ending.

a. Reciclar**íamos**
b. No estar**ían**
c. Comprar**ía**
d. Construir**íais**
e. Habr**ía**
f. Usar**ían**
g. No tirar**íais**
h. Viajar**ía**
i. Esforzar**ías**
j. Deber**ía**
k. Plantar**íamos**

4. Complete.

a. Reciclar**ía**
b. Cambiar**ían**
c. Esperar**íamos**
d. Actuar**íais**
e. Destruir**ían**
f. Reducir**ía**
g. Deber**íamos**
h. Habr**ía**
i. Querr**ía**
j. Podr**ía**
k. Contaminar**ían**

5. Anagrams.

e.g. Reciclarían

a. Reduciríamos
b. Cambiaría
c. Construirían
d. Actuaría
e. Venderían
f. Haríais
g. Viviría

6. Correct.

a. Yo haría
b. Ellos esperarían
c. Vosotros iríais
d. Él querría
e. Nosotros seríamos
f. Yo podría
g. Nosotros viviríamos

7. Translate into Spanish.

a. Reciclaría
b. Cambiaría
c. Haría
d. Debería ser
e. Podría vivir
f. Aumentaría
g. Pararía
h. Compraría

i. Reciclarías
j. Deberíamos consumir
k. Podrían comprar
l. Le gustaría hacer
m. Podríais utilizar
n. Destruirían
o. Podríamos viajar
p. Deberían reducir

8. What would you do…

a. **Plantaría** más árboles.
b. **Viajaría** en tren o en barco.
c. **Iría** andando o en bicicleta.
d. **Organizaría** una manifestación.
e. **Compraría** un coche de hidrógeno.

9. Translate into Spanish.

a. Me gustaría comprar menos ropa.
b. Debería intentar utilizar el coche menos.
c. Cambiaría mis hábitos en el futuro
d. Reciclaríamos papel, plástico y vidrio.
e. Habría menos contaminación.

f. El futuro sería más limpio y mejor.
g. Malgastaría menos energía en casa.
h. Viajaríamos en transporte público.
i. La gente sería más feliz y sana.

Unit 3 Answers
Preparing for speaking and writing

1. Complete with the missing letters.

a. Yo reciclo un poco pero no lo suficiente.

b. Yo utilizo el transporte público tanto como puedo.

c. Las fábricas contaminan.

d. Lo que me preocupa es el calentamiento global.

e. Yo vivo en un pequeño pueblo en el sur.

f. El paisaje alrededor de mi pueblo es bonito.

g. Mi barrio es muy limpio y seguro.

h. Ellos construyen demasiados edificios y autopistas.

2. Anagrams.

a. Reciclaje

b. Agua

c. Ruido

d. Bolsas

e. Destruir

f. Vidrio

g. Paisaje

h. Árboles

3. Complete.

a. Reciclo

b. Voy/monto

c. Soy

d. Malgasto

e. Vivo

f. Hay

g. Reducir

4. Match up.

Basura	Waste
Mar	Sea
Vidrio	Glass
Fábrica	Factory
Amenaza	Threat
Calentamiento	Warming
Edificio	Building
Renovable	Renewable
Lugar	Place
Destruir	To destroy
Tierra	Earth
Árbol	Tree

5. Split sentences.

El mar está muy	contaminado...
Hay que reciclar	los plásticos.
En mi pueblo no hay	mucho que hacer.
Las fábricas	contaminan...
Mi ciudad es	pequeña y bonita.
Lo que me preocupa es	el calentamiento...
Ellos destruyen	el paisaje.
La gente malgasta	los recursos...
Yo utilizo el transporte	público.
La energía solar	va a tener...

6. Complete the trans.

a. Reciclaje...basura.

b. Destrucción...bosques.

c. Malgasto...recursos.

d. Gases...invernadero.

e. Demasiados edificios.

f. Alrededor...pueblo.

g. Barrio...contaminando.

h. Contaminación...mar.

7. *Yo* and *Nosotros*.

Enciendo	Encendemos
Aumento	Aumentamos
Conduzco	Conducimos
Consumo	Consumimos
Malgasto	Malgastamos
Tiro	Tiramos
Contamino	Contaminamos
Reciclo	Reciclamos
Salvo	Salvamos

8. Translation (easier).

a. Vivo en un pueblo pequeño en Inglaterra.

b. Mi pueblo es bonito y limpio.

c. El paisaje cerca de mi pueblo es bonito.

d. Hay muchos árboles y flores.

e. Mi familia recicla papel, vidrio y plásticos.

f. Nunca utilizamos bolsas de plástico.

g. La crisis climática es peligrosa para el planeta.

h. La temperatura sube cada año.

i. El año que viene no voy a viajar en avión.

j. Siempre utilizo el transporte público.

k. No tiro basura al suelo.

l. El sábado reciclé unas botellas.

m. Voy a plantar un árbol.

n. El fin de semana pasado cogí el autobús.

9. Translation (harder).

a. Lo que más me preocupa es el calentamiento global.

b. La contaminación del agua es un gran problema en mi región.

c. Mi ciudad es muy ruidosa, sucia y contaminada.

d. El gobierno debería hacer más.

e. Han construido demasiados edificios y carreteras.

f. Lo peor es la destrucción de los bosques.

g. La gente no recicla su basura lo suficiente.

h. Deberíamos reciclar más y consumir menos agua y electricidad.

i. En mi familia reciclamos basura y evitamos usar demasiada agua.

j. Además nunca utilizamos el coche para viajes cortos.

k. La energía solar debería jugar un papel más importante.

l. Si fuera posible viajaría menos en el avión.

m. Debería intentar no viajar en el avión.

Higher writing
2. Translate the paragraph below.

Me gusta comprar productos ecológicos en el supermercado. Reciclamos muchas cosas cada semana. No viajo en avión. La semana pasada mis amigos y yo fuimos a París en tren. Quiero seguir protegiendo el planeta en el futuro. El medio ambiente es un tema importante para mí.

Unit 4 Answers

Foundation vocab building

1. Match up.

Celebrar	To celebrate
Rezar	To pray
Bailar	To dance
Ofrecer	To give, to offer
Enviar	To send
Recibir	To receive
Compartir	To share
Felicitar	To congratulate
Desear	To wish
Casarse	To marry

2. Complete.

a. Dios

b. Regalo

c. Celebrar

d. Feliz

e. Judío

f. Comida

g. Ofrecer

h. Fiesta

i. El desfile

3. Complete.

a. Church

b. New Year.

c. God

d. Presents

e. Money

f. Muslims

h. Festival

4. Correct order.

a. Una fiesta religiosa.

b. La comida de Navidad.

c. El día de San Valentín.

d. La misa de Pascua.

e. El ayuno de Ramadán.

f. Los fuegos artificiales.

g. Los regalos de Navidad

h. Un templo budista.

i. Mi fiesta favorita.

j. Con toda mi familia.

k. En casa de mis padres.

l. Los Reyes Magos.

5. Spot and correct.

a. Festival

b. Friends

c. "King's Day"

d. Christians

e. Are getting married

f. Celebrate

g. Fireworks

h. Presents

i. Gather

j. Good

6. Tick all religious words.

a. Iglesia √

b. Cristiano √

c. Judío √

d. Gente

e. Regalo

f. Misa √

g. Tiempo

h. Sol

i. Año Nuevo

j. Catedral √

k. Musulmán √

l. Budista √

m. Fiesta

n. Fuegos artificiales

o. Dinero

p. Templo √

q. Mezquita √

r. Dios √

s. Festival

t. Pingüino

7. Wordsearch.

S	T	M	U	S	U	L	M	A	N	E	S	M	R	N	P	Z	F	N	I
F	A	Ñ	O	N	U	E	V	O	R	C	N	E	E	M	A	X	I	A	G
G	P	E	C	O	M	P	A	R	T	I	R	S	D	Z	R	B	E	V	L
F	U	E	G	O	S	A	R	T	I	F	I	C	I	A	L	E	S	I	E
K	W	P	R	O	C	H	E	S	P	Ê	C	T	O	B	A	F	T	D	S
L	D	G	H	U	P	S	K	L	D	T	P	A	S	C	U	A	A	A	I
C	R	I	S	T	I	A	N	O	S	E	P	A	Q	U	E	S	N	D	A
R	O	E	F	S	P	A	R	I	E	N	T	E	S	A	R	E	Z	A	R

8. Complete with the options.

a. Los **fuegos** artificiales.

b. La **gente** va a la iglesia.

c. Prepara la **comida** de Navidad.

d. Yo recibo **regalos**.

e. La gente celebra la **Navidad**.

f. Nosotros **cantamos**.

g. Yo **creo** en Dios.

h. Eid es mi fiesta **favorita**.

i. Yo **celebro** mi cumpleaños con mi familia.

9. Translate into English.

a. You go to church on Sunday.

b. For the New Year there are fireworks.

c. We celebrate Mothers' Day.

d. Jews go to the synagogue.

e. Many people get married in summer.

f. In most towns there are local festivals.

g. There are concerts and parades.

h. Friends gather to have a party.

i. I celebrate my birthday with my friends.

Foundation reading

1. a) Eva   b) Sandra   c) Eva   d) Pablo   e) Sandra   f) Pablo

2. a) Martina   b) Daniela   c) Andrés   d) Antonio

3. a) Last September   b) Once a year   c) Environment in Colombia   d) Sowing trees   e) A local artisan product

4. a) A Chilean indigenous festival   b) January   c) Chilean and foreign singers   d) November   e) South

5. Adam N   Estefania PN   Martin P   Camila PN   Benjamin P

6. 1c 2b 3c 4c

Unit 4 Answers
Higher vocab building

1. Match up.

Desfile	Parade	**Cantar**	To sing
Pascua	Easter	**Ofrecer**	To offer
Fiesta	Party	**Contento**	Happy
Año Nuevo	New Year	**Boda**	Wedding
Musulmán	Muslim	**Rezar**	To pray
Gente	People	**Comida**	Meal
Iglesia	Church	**Enviar**	To send
Cristianos	Christians	**Creer**	To believe
Día festivo	Public holiday	**Fe**	Faith
Niños	Children	**Recibir**	To receive
Regalos	Gifts	**Evento**	Event
Familiares	Relatives	**Felicidad**	Happiness

2. Gapped translation.

a. Celebrate New Year.

b. Christians... church.

c. People... presents.

d. Enjoy... holidays.

e. See... relatives.

f. Family... in my home.

g. Believe... God.

3. Spot and correct.

a. New Year's Day.
b. Congratulate.
c. Gather.
d. Mad/crazy.
e. Good.
f. Meal.
g. Muslim.
h. Sing.
i. Time.
j. Relatives.
k. Mothers' Day.
l. We.

4. Sentence puzzle.

1. Yo celebro la Navidad comprando regalos.

2. Acabamos de estar en un gran festival de música.

3. Si yo fuera religioso iría a la iglesia.

4. Nosotros no celebramos la Pascua en casa.

5. En mi opinión es importante mantener las tradiciones.

6. Yo espero ir al festival de Diwali en octubre.

5. Definitions.

a. Eid.
b. Pascua.
c. Regalos.
d. San Valentín.
e. Celebrar.
f. Sinagoga.
g. Iglesia.
h. Navidad.
i. Preferido.
j. Regalar.

6. Split sentences.

Yo creo en Dios.
Ellos celebran el Año Nuevo en mi casa.
Nosotros vamos a la misa de Pascua.
Yo ofrezco regalos.
Ella se casa con Felipe.
Nosotros nos reunimos en mi casa.
Compartimos un buen momento juntos.
Hay fuegos artificales.
Veo a mis familiares.

7. Translate into English.

a. A present.
b. My God.
c. (The) fireworks.
d. A public holiday.
e. (The) Christmas cake.
f. A day of joy.
g. We share.
h. They give.
i. I receive.
j. We gather.

8. Translate into English.

a. The Three Kings' Day is in January.
b. Every year Muslims celebrate Eid.
c. Friends gather to have a good time.
d. These special occasions are often public holidays.
e. In most towns there are parades.
f. At Easter we always eat chocolate eggs.
g. I love to watch fireworks at New Year.
h. I love Christmas because it is my favourite festival.
i. I give presents to my parents.

Higher reading

1. a) July and August   b) Traditional flower making   c) Traditional costumes   d) There is a contest for the best creation

2. a) N   b) F   c) P   d) F

3. 1b   2a   3c

4. a) A city   b) Shrine   c) Latin America   d) Book a hotel in advance – lots of visitors   e) Burning

5. a) 1 day   b) Beautiful white dress   c) Ask her father for the bride-to-be's hand   d) Civil...few days...dos fiestas

6. a) Answer all questions people ask you.   b) How many children do you have? How old are you? What do you do for a living?

   c) Take an afternoon nap or watch TV.   d) After the sunset.   e) They are a couple.   f) Baptism

7. a) She was religious/believed in God – no longer believes   b) When a child is born & there is a baptism.   c) Her sister's wedding.

Unit 4 Answers
Grammar focus – Present Tense

PRES	I receive a lot of presents.
PAST	I have received three birthday presents.
PRES	Usually I celebrate Easter in April.
PAST	Yesterday I celebrated my birthday.
PAST	We went to the science festival.
PRES	I always give presents.
PAST	My mother has made me a beautiful present.
FUT	My friends are going to a party tomorrow.
PRES	We go to the synagogue often.
PRES	I love to do celebrations with my friends.
PAST	My parents loved celebrating Christmas.
FUT	My friends are going to go to a festival next Saturday.
PAST	I have gone to a synagogue with my parents.
PRES	I go to a mosque to pray.
PAST	The festival was amazing.

1. Match up.

Recibir	To receive
Desear	To wish
Celebrar	To celebrate
Querer	To want
Dar	To give
Ver	To see
Conocer	To meet
Salir	To go out
Creer	To believe
Ofrecer	To offer
Visitar	To visit
Tomar	To take
Comprar	To buy
Ayunar	To fast

2. Complete.

a. Compro
b. Visito
c. Veo
d. Quiero
e. Como
f. Salgo
g. Celebro
h. Creo

3. Circle the correct form of the verb.

a. Vender: yo vendo
b. Recibir: recibes
c. Celebrar: celebra
d. Creer: creemos
e. Ofrecer: ofrezco
f. Engordar: engorda
g. Elegir: elegís
h. Tomar: toman
i. Regalar: regala
j. Salir: salimos
k. Visitar: visitan
l. Comprar: compras
m. Asistir: asistís
n. Deber: debe

4. Translate.

a. I receive.
b. You visit.
c. You offer/give.
d. You celebrate.
e. He chooses.
f. You go out.

5. Add the missing letters.

a. Ponemos
b. Va
c. Hacemos
d. Vengo
e. Eliges
f. Terminamos
g. Esperan
h. ¿Qué haces?
i. Engordo
j. Visitais
k. Compra
l. Como

6. Complete.

a. Come
b. Vais
c. Visita
d. Recibes
e. Salgo
f. Compráis

7. Insert Yo, Tu, Ella, Nosotros, Vosotros o Ellos as appropriate.

a. **Nosotros** vamos a ponernos un traje.
b. **Ellos** reciben regalos.
c. **Yo** como muchos pasteles.
d. ¿Qué hacen **ellos** en Navidad?
e. **Vosotros** celebráis Yom Kipur.
f. Durante Eid **ella** ayuna.
g. En Navidad **nosotros** comemos mucho.
h. **Ella** no cree en Dios.
i. **Ellos** no quieren regalos.
j. **Vosotros** bebéis mucha cava.
k. **Yo** voy a casa en Nochebuena.
l. **Ellos** van a pasar las vacaciones en Cuba.
m. **Ella** va a la sinagoga con sus padres.
n. **Nosotros** nos quedamos en casa.
o. ¿Visita **ella** a sus padres?
p. ¿**Tú** ves a tus primos?

8. Translate into Spanish.

a. Nosotros metemos/ponemos
b. Yo voy
c. Ella espera
d. Ellos visitan
e. Nosotros comemos
f. Ellos/ellas ayunan
g. Nosotros recibimos
h. Yo tomo
i. Ella quiere/desea
j. Yo rezo
k. ¿Tú ves?
l. Nosotros celebramos
m. Yo veo
n. Ellos/ellas dan
o. Yo creo

9. Translate into Spanish (easier).

a. Ellas van a la iglesia.
b. Ella sale mucho.
c. Nos quedamos en casa.
d. Ellos comen mariscos.
e. Yo recibo regalos.
f. Nosotros celebramos en casa.
g. ¿Tú crees en Dios?
h. Siempre veo el desfile.
i. Rezamos y ayunamos.

10. Translate into Spanish (harder).

a. En Navidad damos y recibimos muchos regalos.
b. Nunca voy a los grandes festivales de música.
c. Ellos celebran la Pascua en casa.
d. Creo que es importante mantener las tradiciones.
e. Queremos ir al festival de Diwali la semana que viene.
f. Después de dar los regalos, normalmente comemos juntos.
g. La ciudad organiza un festival cada año.
h. Cada año vamos a ver la procesión de Semana Santa / Pascua.
i. Acabo de comprar un regalo para mi amigo.
j. El día de San Valentín es la tradición que menos me gusta.

Unit 4 Answers
Preparing for speaking and writing

1. Match up.

Yo celebro	I celebrate
Yo doy	I give
Yo como	I eat
Yo voy	I go
Yo descanso	I rest
Yo disfruto	I enjoy
Yo felicito	I congratulate
Yo descubro	I discover
Yo veo	I see
Yo quedo con	I meet up with
Yo recibo	I receive
Yo me quedo	I stay
Yo ayuno	I fast

2. Complete with a suitable verb.

a. En casa **celebro** la Navidad pero no la Pascua.

b. **Felicito** a mis familiares.

c. **Descanso** en mi casa.

d. **Disfruto** de las vacaciones.

e. **Me quedo** en casa de mis abuelos.

f. **Como** pavo.

g. **Voy** en una semana a Costa Rica.

h. **Doy** y recibo regalos.

3. Anagrams.

a. Su dios
b. Una fiesta
c. En Navidad
d. Yo voy
e. En mi casa
f. Nosotros gastamos
g. El próximo verano
h. En Pascua
i. Un regalo
j. Una procesión
k. Una gran comida
l. Fuegos artificales

4. Broken words.

a. Dur**ante**
b. F**iesta**
c. Yo ga**sto**
d. En mi **casa**
e. Con mi fam**ilia**
f. Nosotros **vemos**
g. Yo qu**edo**
h. Ce**lebramos**

5. Complete the table.

Infinitive	Present	Perfect tense
Pasar	Yo paso	Yo he pasado
Ir	Yo voy	Yo he ido
Descansar	Yo	Yo he
Dar	Yo doy	Yo he dado
Disfrutar	Yo disfruto	Yo he disfrutado
Ver	Yo veo	Yo he visto
Celebrar	Yo celebro	Yo he celebrado
Recibir	Yo recibo	Yo he recibido

6. Complete the translation.

a. Yo **paso** las vacaciones de Navidad en mi **casa**.

b. En **Pascua** voy a la **iglesia**.

c. Hay **fuegos** artificiales y una gran **procesión**.

d. Normalmente voy a la m**ezquita** para **rezar**.

e. Nosotros d**amos** y **recibimos regalos**.

f. Yom Kipur en una f**iesta judía**.

g. Nuestros f**amiliares** se reúnen en n**uestra** casa.

7. Missing accents.

a. Vosotros celebráis
b. Las últimas vacaciones
c. Musulmán
d. Una fiesta judía
e. Una celebración religiosa
f. Católico
g. Una tradición española
h. El Día de la Madre
i. El Roscón de Reyes

8. Sentence puzzle.

a. Eid es una fiesta musulmana.
b. A menudo hay desfiles.
c. Nosotros comemos dulces navideños.
d. Yo doy y recibo regalos.
e. Mi fiesta favorita es Navidad
f. La gente compra regalos.
g. Yo veo a mis familiares y amigos.

9. Translate into Spanish.

a. Voy a la iglesia con mis padres.
b. Recibimos algunos regalos.
c. Hay fuegos artificiales en el parque.
d. Celebro Eid con mi familia.
e. Celebramos la Navidad cada año.
f. Visito a mis abuelos en Pascua.
g. Paso la Pascua en casa en abril.
h. Como muchos dulces navideños.
i. Ayuno y rezo en la mezquita.
j. Mis familiares se reúnen en mi casa.
k. Celebro Yom Kipur con mi familia.
l. Mi fiesta favorita es Diwali.

10. Translate into Spanish.

a. En Navidad mis amigos y familiares se reúnen en mi casa para celebrar juntos.

b. En muchos pueblos en España hay procesiones y fuegos artificiales para celebrar esta fiesta.

c. Es mi fiesta favorita porque recibo muchos regalos de mis padres y familiares.

d. Normalmente no voy a ningún lado durante las vacaciones. Me quedo en casa, veo la tele y como mucho.

e. Me encantan las fiestas nacionales porque no tenemos que ir al colegio y hacer deberes.

f. En mi región hay muchas cosas para ver por lo que durante las vacaciones salimos mucho.

g. Durante esta fiesta ayuno, voy a la mezquita y rezo.

Unit 5 Answers

Foundation vocab building

1. Match up.

Red	Network
Juego	Game
Publicar	To post
Móvil	Mobile phone
Ordenador	Computer
Preocupante	Worrying
Comprar	To buy
Nuevo	New
Herramienta	Tool
Disponible	Available
En línea	Online
Descargar	To download
Pantalla	Screen
Programa	Programme
Robar	To steal
Juventud	Youth
Subir	To upload

2. Translate.

a. Computer
b. Tool
c. Screen
d. New
e. Network
f. Game
g. Programme
h. To follow
i. Mobile phone
j. To share
k. Word
l. Safe
m. To send
n. Digital

3. Anagrams.

a. Herramienta
b. Juego
c. Comprar
d. Seguir
e. Subir
f. Disponible
g. Grabar
h. Pantalla
i. Nuevo

4. Correct the translation.

a. Social **networks**
b. **Online** games
c. A digital **tool**
d. A new **computer**
e. My old **mobile phone**
f. To **buy** digital devices
g. A new **TV programme**
h. A new **screen**
i. To **stay** connected
j. To **share** photos
k. To **download** a programme
l. A **worrying** problem

5. Break the flow.

a. Es más rápido.
b. Yo navego por internet.
c. Yo sigo a algunos influencers.
d. Comparto fotos en Instagram.
e. Un peligro de internet.
f. Es más fácil comunicarse.
g. Paso un montón de tiempo.
h. En mi móvil y en mi ordenador.

6. Split words.

Memoria (Memory)
Redes (Networks)
Compartir (Share)
Subir (Upload)
Pantalla (Screen)
Fácil (Easy)
Funcionar (To work)
Robar (To steal)
Seguir (To follow)
Juego (Game)

7. Correct order.

a. Yo tengo un móvil nuevo.
b. Es más fácil comunicarse.
c. Yo a menudo comparto fotos en Instagram.
d. Yo me conecto a internet todos los días.
e. Hay muchos peligros en internet.

8. Translate into English.

a. On my mobile.
b. I spend a lot of time.
c. I love chatting.
d. I share photos.
e. I'm going to buy.
f. I listen to some songs.
g. (The) social networks.
h. I send SMS.

9. Translate into English.

a. Instagram is my favourite social network.
b. I share lots of photos on Facebook.
c. I love to chat with my friends online.
d. One danger of the internet is identity theft.
e. Yesterday I uploaded a video to YouTube.
f. I spend a lot of time on my computer.
g. I always do all my homework on my computer.
h. Tomorrow I'm going to buy a USB stick.
i. Social networks are addictive.
j. I follow several influencers on TikTok because they are funny.
k. I don't like Facebook. It's not cool.
l. I love to watch videos on YouTube.

Foundation reading

1. a) Juan   b) Raúl   c) Paula   d) Raúl   e) Paula   f) Juan
2. 1b   2a   3b
3. a) David   b) Emma   c) Carmen   d) Sergio
4. a) Puts people in touch with each other.   b) Clothing – shelter – to talk – to have a coffee.   c) How to meet people on the street.
   d) 1000 people found other people.
5. a) N   b) P   c) F
6. Correct answers are a, b, f, h
7. a, d, e
8. Doesn't share passwords – Doesn't download unfamiliar programmes – Buys nothing online when on public wifi.

Unit 5 Answers
Higher vocab building

1. Match up.

Enviar	To send
Encender	To turn on
Emitir	To broadcast
Grabar	To record
Descargar	To download
Traducir	To translate
Reproducir	To play
Leer	To read
Ver	To watch
Recibir	To receive
Seguir	To follow
Apagar	To turn off
Comprar	To buy

2. Complete.

a. Envío

b. Veo

c. Juego

d. Enciendo

e. Hago

f. Soy

g. Comparto

h. Compro

3. Spot and correct.

a. I like to play on my **computer.**

b. I turn **off**...

c. I **often** go on...

d. I **share** photos...

e. I **follow** some...

f. I **send**... **to** him.

g. It's a good **tool.**

h. It is no... **online.**

i. I am...**mobile.**

4. Split sentences.

Juego y...	mi ordenador.
Mi tema...	la informática.
internet...	al robo...
Hago...	con mi móvil.
Sigo...	de deporte...
Me gusta...	videos en...
WordRef...	herramienta...
El robo...	tema...
Apple...	de ordenador...
Creo que...	son...

5. Gapped trans.

a. Digital

b. Just

c. Anything

d. Social media

e. Worries

f. Theft

g. Future

h. Searching

i. Download

j. Share

k. Read

l. Less

6. Match the opposites.

Enciendo	Apago
Caro	Barato
Seguro	Peligroso
Yo envío	Yo recibo
Fácil	Difícil
Actual	Pasado
Yo compro	Yo vendo
Nada	Todo
Joven	Viejo
Disminuir	Aumentar

7. One of three. Circle the right translation.

Seguro			Safe
Funcionar		To work	
Actual			Current
Encender	To turn on		
Joven		Young	
Disponible	Available		
Robar			To steal
Enviar	To send		
Palabra		Word	
Compra	Purchase		

8. Translate.

a. Online shopping.

b. To turn on the computer.

c. To buy a mobile phone.

d. Addicted to social media.

e. To send text messages.

f. Offensive words.

9. Translate into English.

a. Many young people today are addicted to social media.

b. Teens spend a lot of time on the internet.

c. What is worrying is that identity theft is very common.

d. The internet is not a safe space. There are many dangers.

e. The mobile phone is a powerful means of communication.

f. New technologies make communication easier.

g. Thanks to the internet, you can shop and play online.

h. We can stay in touch with people who live far away.

i. I learn a lot by looking for information online.

J. I never use on social media anymore.

Higher reading

1. a) Old people with memory problems.   b) It tells people when to take their medicine.   c) You can check on the app if you have taken the medicine or not.   d) A good example of tech helping people in their daily lives.

2. a) Children with sight problems.   b) Translates written texts into sign language.   c) It's free.   d) Identify children with hearing problems – suggests possible treatments.   e) People with visual impairment.   f) Identify someone's emotions by scanning their face and position of their eyes, nose, and mouth.

3. a) P   b) N   c) PN   d) P   e) N

4. a) In two centuries (200 years).   b) On a planet far from Earth.   c) By thought.   d) Whether to help her husband kill someone.

5. a) N   b) P   c) F   d) N

6. a) Clara   b) Laura   c) Laura   d) Samuel   e) Samuel   f) Samuel

Unit 5 Answers
Grammar focus – negatives

Translate - Part 1
a. I don´t like videogames.
b. I never download movies.
c. I don´t buy new clothes.
d. I don´t sell anything on internet.
e. I only buy books.
f. I don´t know anyone online.

Translate - Part 2
a. I don't like to buy (things) on the internet.
b. I am never going to watch that series again.
c. I must not share my passwords.
d. I don't want to buy a new computer.

Translate - Part 3
a. Before I used to eat meat, but not anymore.
b. I don't have time anymore to go to the gym.
c. Before I used to like pop music, but not anymore.
d. I don´t watch cartoons anymore.

1. Sentence puzzle.

a. Yo no chateo en línea con nadie.

b. Ya no salgo con mis amigos.

c. No compro en línea.

d. Ya no uso las redes sociales.

e. Creo que no hay nada interesante en la tele.

f. Ya no voy al cine con mis padres.

g. No descargo vídeos muy a menudo.

h. Nunca juego a videojuegos.

2. Complete.

a. Nunca

b. No

c. Nadie

d. Ya

e. Nada

f. Nadie

3. Spot and correct the mistakes.

a. **No** conozco a nadie sin móvil.

b. **Yo** nunca uso internet.

c. **Nadie** juega conmigo.

d. **No** veo nunca series de televisión.

e. **Ya no** uso Snapchat

f. **No tengo** móvil.

g. **Nadie** chatea conmigo.

h. **No** compro nada por internet.

i. **Ya** no tengo cuenta en X.

4. Make the sentences negative (other options are valid).
a. No compro regalos.
b. Ya no veo la tele.
c. Nunca descargo películas.
d. No uso Instagram.
e. Ya no sigo a varios influencers.
f. No me conecto a menudo.
g. Ya no me gustan los programas de telerrealidad.

5. Complete the table.

a. Compré

b. Usé

c. Chateé

d. Bajé

e. Me conecté

f. Apagué

g. No me metí

h. Compartí

i. Publiqué

6. Split sentences.

No compro	nada en línea.
Nunca juego	a la PlayStation.
No sigo	a nadie en IG.
No tengo	muchos amigos.
No utilizo	mi cuenta en Snap.
Yo chateo	por WhatsApp.
No	descargo vídeos.
No me gusta	Facebook.
No paso	mucho tiempo en X

7. Translate into Spanish.
a. No conozco a nadie.

b. No compro nada.

c. Ya no juego.

d. No paso mucho tiempo.

e. A nadie le gusta Facebook.

8. Translate into Spanish.
a. Nunca juego juegos en línea.

b. Paso muchas horas en línea cada día.

c. No chateo con nadie en línea.

d. Nunca uso las redes sociales.

e. No hay nada interesante en la tele.

f. Nunca sigo a nadie en Instagram.

g. Nunca he comprado nada en línea.

h. Nunca descargo aplicaciones.

i. Normalmente no veo los vídeos en YouTube.

j. Nunca he seguido a ningún influencer.

Unit 5 Answers
Preparing for speaking and writing

1. Complete.

a. El ordenador

b. La herramienta

c. Traducir

d. Los jóvenes

e. El móvil

f. La red

g. Descargar

h. La pantalla

i. Funcionar

j. Las compras

k. En línea

l. Jugar

2. Complete with the missing words.

a. Yo uso mi **móvil** para conectarme a internet.

b. Ayer vi una película de acción **en** Netflix.

c. No me gusta la **publicidad**. Es molesta.

d. Yo **hago/saco** muchas fotos con mi teléfono.

e. Me encanta **chatear** con mis compañeros por WhatsApp.

f. Yo comparto **fotos** por Instagram con frecuencia.

g. ¿**Pasas** (tú) mucho tiempo en las redes sociales?

h. El sábado por la noche vi un **programa** de música genial.

i. El fin de semana **que viene** voy a descansar en casa.

j. Voy a **jugar** a la PlayStation con mi hermano.

3. Translate into Spanish.

a. Me encanta

b. Mi móvil

c. Un programa

d. Las redes sociales

e. Delante de la pantalla

f. Mi página web favorita

g. Una herramienta digital

h. En línea

i. Los jóvenes

j. Yo descargo

k. Yo comparto

l. Yo tomo

m. La tecnología

n. Los juegos en línea

4. Complete the table.

Present	Preterite	Future
Yo veo	Yo vi	Yo voy a ver
Yo juego	Yo jugué	Yo voy a jugar
Yo descargo	Descargué	Voy a descargar
Yo comparto	Yo compartí	Voy a compartir
Yo apago	Yo apagué	Yo voy a apagar
Yo envío	Yo envié	Yo voy a enviar
Yo hago	Yo hice	Yo voy a hacer
Yo tomo	Yo tomé	Yo voy a tomar

5. Tangled translation.

a. Nada

b. Rompí...móvil

c. Voy a...con...en línea

d. Favorita

e. Nunca...en

f. Compartir...en

g. Veo...programas...en

6. Complete with a suitable verb.

a. Hago/saco/tomo

b. Veo

c. Hablo/salgo/juego

d. Escucho/comparto/descargo

e. Juego

f. Escribo/envío/mando

g. Uso/utilizo

7. Correct the Spanish translations below.

a. **Paso** mucho tiempo en internet.

b. Esta **noche** voy a chatear.

c. Hoy me he comprado un **ordenador** nuevo.

d. Juego **en línea** todos los días.

e. Uso mi **móvil** para tomar fotos.

f. **He descargado** algunos vídeos divertidos.

g. Hay **muchos** peligros en internet.

h. **Compartí** muchas fotos en Instagram.

8. Translate into Spanish.

a. Me encanta mi móvil.

b. Uso WhatsApp a menudo.

c. Mi página web favorita es...

d. Odio a los juegos en línea.

e. Las aplicaciones de música son buenas.

f. Hago compras en línea.

g. Uso mucho internet.

h. Descargo vídeos.

i. Comparto fotos.

9. Translate into Spanish.

a. Uso/Utilizo mi teléfono para tomar fotos.

b. Comparto fotos y vídeos.

c. Envío mensajes por WhatsApp.

d. Mi red social favorita es TikTok.

e. Paso mucho tiempo con mi teléfono.

f. Nunca hago mis deberes en mi ordenador.

g. Uso/Utilizo mi ordenador para buscar información.

h. Nunca bajo/descargo música.

i. Uso/Utilizo mi (teléfono) móvil para hacer/sacar/tomar fotos.

j. Compro cosas por internet porque es rápido.

k. Los adolescentes pasan demasiado tiempo con sus móviles.

l. Prefiero los podcasts a la radio tradicional.

m. El domingo pasado descargué una nueva aplicación de música.

n. Mañana voy a empezar una nueva serie en Netflix.

o. Este fin de semana voy a charlar/chatear con mi amigo.

p. Voy a ver un programa musical realmente genial.

Printed in Great Britain
by Amazon